D1591012

ANTI-MATTER

C.M. Stanbury

PS
3569
T3315
A8x

Glossary – P. 109

Cover by George Mattingly

$2.95/paper   ISBN 0-913218-54-5
$7.95/cloth   ISBN 0-913218-55-3

Copyright © 1977 by C.M. Stanbury

The "American Dust" Series, No. 7

First Printing, January 1977
Published by Dustbooks, P.O. Box 1056, Paradise,
CA 95969

Library of Congress Cataloging in Publication Data

Stanbury, C   M
    Anti-matter.

    (The American dust series ; no. 7)
I. Title.
PZ4.S786An   [PS3569.T3315]   813'.5.4   76-30638
ISBN 0-913218-55-3
ISBN 0-913218-54-5 pbk.

Some Notes From The Author

Since the late 1950s, I have been a pulp writer and damn satisfied with it too. Because in a pulp magazine, whether it was *Marvel Tales* or *Electronics Illustrated*, if he knew how, the writer could reach a mass audience with material that was at least of some significance, and the editor didn't give a shit so long as your material sold copies and didn't disparage an advertiser's product.

Pulp was heaven for a pro—whatever his specialty. Mine was electronics: an appropriate cliche would be that I lived, ate and breathed pulp electronics including some down right "subversive" science fiction for the now defunct *Radio-TV Experimenter*.

Actually all of pulp, especially the relatively high paying how-to/hobby/quasi-scientific and technical magazines, is defunct, or near to it, as a useful mass media. There is the surface evidence of demise: those books still operating in this current economy feature articles which are often indistinguishable from advertising.

"Financially oriented executives are taking over where traditionalist genteel editors used to hold sway" cooed *Business Week*....this executive's forays into editorial decisions functioned to undermine the editors' confidence and autonomy."

—Richard Kostelanetz, The End of Intelligent Writing",
DECEMBER, vol. 13

But pulp is not "genteel" and any good pulp man could have coped with the escalated hype except that pulp editors suddenly became genteel, somewhat in the style of *Creep,* or much in the same way that the modern ad man is educated. If the producers of TV's private eye shows (the current broadcast equivalent of pulp) ever become this sophisticated, under fire from the sex and violence front organizations, we could have a police state over night. It could be, of course, that editors don't have anything to say about it in this era of corporate greed.

In any event, the resultant pulp product has become as bland and amoral as Billy Graham and Ronald MacDonald (both ardent Nixon supporters).

The new pulp ethics apply not only to political and sociological issues but, apparently, to technological questions as well. Kostelanetz in "The End of Intelligent Writing" suggests the only alternative is the small ("independent") presses. But it is not merely a matter of "new" literature. It is a matter of survival.

Anti-Matter is a small press exploration of pulp America as it has evolved over the last decade. A journey to the edge, or is it the center, and possibly the end of the Gutenberg galaxy.

Since the Bay of Pigs debacle, a small band of writers has made a living by churning out books on the Central Intelligence Agency. Although their works also appear in slick and even quasi-intellectual journals, these books are basically as pulpish as "Chariots of the Gods". Typical of this genre is Tad Szulc's "Compulsive Spy" which was rushed into print in 1974.

"The State Department asked the CIA to keep Hunt's name out of any future appointments to diplomatic missions. Richard Helms, the new director of the CIA replacing Dulles, fought hard for Hunt, but it was to no avail. The best that could be done for Hunt in 1963 was to assign him as acting chief of the CIA's Mexico City station during August and September".

Even for books on the CIA, this is an astounding bit of misinformation. Helms did not follow Dulles as Director of the CIA, John McCone did. McCone served until 1965. He was John Kennedy's handpicked man to clean up the Agency in the wake of Bahia Cochinas. During his reign, the CIA's liberals would have been running the show. It is inconceivable that McCone "fought hard" for E.Howard Hunt.

Equally glaring is that nowhere in "Compulsive Spy" does Szulc reveal, presumably because he didn't know, Hunt's primary assignment during the years which followed the Bay of Pigs. According to secret Hunt testimony before the Senate Watergate committee, subsequently published by the *New York Times*, he was responsible for manipulation of news and publishing organizations. Even the Rockefeller report acknowledges Hunt "was assigned to duty in Washington, D.C., performing work related to propaganda operations in foreign countries. His duties included travel to other cities in the United States".

The post-Watergate products of this genre have become so generally inaccurate, so wildly biased, as to be absolutely harmless. They provide the reader with a fantasy trip. Although in an opposite direction, they are as far from factual reality as "The Man From UNCLE" and "The Wild Wild West" were in the 1960s.

In July 1975 ex-USAF Colonel L. Fletcher Prouty, AMTRAC PR man, author of his own expose book ("The Secret Team"), and arch CIA hater, accused Alexander Butterfield of being a CIA contact. Butterfield is the man who revealed the existence of the White House tapes. He is the man who finished what former CIA Agent James McCord (fund raiser for the Committee to Investigate Assassinations) began when he bungled the Watergate break-in—the destruction of Richard Nixon. Among other things, Prouty says E. Howard Hunt told him so.

After the Prouty charge, Fred Thompson, former Minority Council to the Senate Watergate Committee, said that his investigators received similar information in 1973 but the committee didn't consider it particularly important at the time. Butterfield is also the only major government figure to publicly accuse Nixon of having personally ordered the break-in. Even while denying all CIA connections, Butterfield repeated this thesis and further claimed that he was fired as head of the Federal Aviation Agency by Gerald Ford at the behest of Mr. Nixon, an act of revenge on Nixon's part.

"If there was an assassination conspiracy, it will be the Central Intelligence Agency, or what was the CIA prior to Nixon's election in 1968, which will revenge it. Not an expose but revenge. . . . If in fact the whole Watergate affair is in reality a vendetta launched by the liberal establishment which formerly used the Central Intelligence Agency as its international power base, against a rightist, Pentagon-oriented president. . . ."—SPR #22

Shortly before we wrote the above, Colonel Prouty, probably the only man in American history to combine corporate advertising with radical politics, was suggesting in the Oct. '73 *Ramparts* that Nixon might be at least partially innocent:

"It would be a grave turn of events to learn that President Nixon did know and did endorse and participate in Watergate. It would be much worse to find out that he did not know anything about it: that would mean things had gotten so far out of hand that those men whom he trusted and who were running the White House and its political and governmental activities did so without his knowledge and approval. . . . If Eisenhower did not know about the U-2 conspiracy, Kennedy very likely ran afoul of a deeper conspiracy, as LBJ's ambiguous statement suggests. It resulted in his death. . . . A look at the power and the history of the 15 years lying

5

behind Watergate—at the CIA and the espionage establishment tied to Gordon Liddy's bungling burglars and the bright young men who prepared Gestapo-like plans for the White House—suggests there was indeed a conspiracy—possibly whose reach extended beyond CREEP and even the White House itself".

If Butterfield was the CIA's man in the White House, it is just as reasonable (or unreasonable) to argue that Colonel Prouty is a Pentagon hatchet man—but why use a PR assassin? Why not simply let the expert right winger on the Rockefeller Commission, General Lyman Lemintzer (Chairman of the Joint Chiefs of Staff during the Bay of Pigs and Cuban missile crises) force a legitimate expose of CIA power and the abuse of that power? Because probably no one on that commission dared expose rival power structures. Certainly General Lemintzer was in no position to rock the boat. Lemintzer is a co-chairman of the American Security Council's National Strategy Committee. During the very period that Lemintzer was serving on the Rockefeller Commission, his ASC was attempting to pursuade the oldest, most famous and traditionally non-political missionary shortwave station in the world, HCJB (Quito, Ecuador) to use its facilities for right wing political broadcasts—Radio Americas Libre—broadcasts whose purpose was the overthrow of the government in neighboring Peru.

HCJB in fact refused to carry Radio Americas Libre but this did not deter Lemintzer's American Security Council from telling prospective contributors that HCJB was carrying the program. One major missionary organization which did carry RAL was the Far East Broadcasting Co. It was aired by FEBC's San Francisco station, KGEI, for a few years beginning about 1968, but KGEI ceased doing so around 1973 which is about the time that Watergate broke open. 1973 is also the year of the Chilean coup. As of July 1975 the American Security Council was still sending KGEI its tapes (despite three notices of discontinuence) and was still claiming KGEI as one of its stations. Another station which ASC claimed as a Radio Americas Libre outlet was "The Evening Star Broadcasting Co...Washington, D.C." which is WMAL. The station flatly denies ever carrying Radio Americas Libre. What we have then is a mixture of a right wing fantasy trip and an old fashioned evangelistic ripoff.

When we learned of Radio Americas Libre in the spring of 1975, we received a tentative go ahead from an editor to do an article on it. In the fall of 1974 his magazine had published one of our articles on E.Howard Hunt and the Bay of Pigs/Cuban missile crisis stations, Radio Swan and Radio Americas. In the 1960s an article on Radio Americas Libre would have been readily published by any of the electronics magazines, especially with the Lemintzer and Rockefeller Commission tie in. But the material was not "harmless" and when we finished the article in August, it was promptly rejected. No reason was given for that rejection (possibly the editor wasn't permitted to tell us why). Ironically, the rejection arrived August 29—the very day that the President of Peru was removed by coup. Not the sudden 1973 Chile-style shift from Marxist left to fascist right, but something more subtle, orderly, vague, shadowy, business as usual....bloodless as a vampire at sunset. (That night HCJB described the new Peruvian leader as more conservative and more nationalistic.)

"Scientists now have reasoned: could the Siberian explosion be linked to this strange phenomenon? Could a sizeable chunk of anti-matter possibly have seeped into our galaxy and have exploded in the air before crashing to earth?"—K.C. Kirkbridge,

Radio-TV Experimenter, Jan.1966

—CMS

The Earth Paradox

I—IN SEARCH OF THRUSH

The inter-galactic liner Star Trek 7 arrived at Port Vonnegut on Titan, a moon of Sol 6 ("Saturn", or "Nixon" as it was known in the 30th century) at 2200 UT and the Institute's shuttle Inner Earth 2 picked me up at 1000 the following morning. Overnight accommodations had been made for me at the Atlantis which is on the city's main square facing their statue of the 20th century satirist Kurt Vonnegut.

Vonnegut is of course symptomatic of what every archaeologist faces when he attempts to unravel the enigmas of 20th century Sol 3 (Earth, Terra, Hell—whichever name you choose). Fact and myth are hopelessly interlocked. Backed up with what seems to be equally authentic documentation we have tales of the infamous Nixon, Ironside (a wheelchair detective whom it seems was also the governor of an American state), soul music groups such as Gladys Knight and the Pips who apparently were treated like visiting royalty where ever they entertained, E. Howard Hunt who rivalled Vonnegut as the master of American literature in the 1970s, T.X. Thrush the notorious guerilla leader, UNCLE, an expionage organization—one of many which fought Thrush (and sometimes known as the Federal Bureau of Investigation), cheap newsstand periodicals such as *Popular Electronics* and *Radio-TV Experimenter*, and even a fictitoius media—short wave facsimile—the major prop of an evangelist who called himself "Orpheus".

Looking at the Sol 3 wasteland it is hard to understand how humanity even survived here let alone developed technology sufficient to conquermost of the universe. The alleged Thrush records, a montage of video tapes which somehow also involve Orpheus, were found at a site known as Brentwood on Long Island—just east of the ruins of New York City. My assignment is to authenticate those tapes.

We already know that Orpheus, like Vonnegut, made a literary voyage of discovery to Titan—Vonnegut in 1959 (*The Sirens of Titan*) and Orpheus in 1969 ("The Temptress, The Towers and The Gold", a *Radio-TV Experimenter* short story). Vonnegut found an absurd, machine-like creature which had been implicated in the manipulation of man since the dawn of civilization. Orpheus found Titania, a beautiful but almost transparent (in this respect not unlike Howard Hunt's mistresses) humanoid Wonder Woman planning to conquer Earth by infiltrating its power structures with radio broadcast controlled androids. Vonnegut showed little interest in scientific detail while Orpheus' work was devoted entirely to technological evolution, especially as it affected communications. Despite Vonnegut's religious concerns, he could never have become a culture hero because he offered no new technological innovation such as Orpheus' concept of short wave facsimilie broadcasting as a global, revolutionary mass media. The fictional religion established by Vonnegut's Niles Rumford in *Sirens of Titan* was so lacking in technological system as to have a life span of almost nil. In contrast, the new technologies developed on Sol 3 during the 20th century, which culminated in the first lunar landing during the initial Nixon presidency did in fact open up whole new religious vistas which have engulfed the universe.

Because of the enormity of what I might find at Brentwood, I was unable to sleep on Titan. I knew I wouldn't be able to sleep and spent that night in the Atlantis bar which has been decorated in 20th century decor with soul music, waitresses dressed as black Wonder Women and authentic gin. at 0800 I took a detox pill and had breakfast.

The main Institute "dig" had been at New York City itself. Two junior researchers and a construction crew were dispatched to Long Island—primarily for the purpose of establishing a second, larger landing pod. When a copy of the October 1974 *Popular Electronics* was unearthed all construction came to a halt and the senior people from NYC hurried out. A few days later they sent for me.

Before flying from Heaven out to the Sol system, I made courtesy calls on the Chairman of the Joint Chiefs of Staff, the Director of the Central Intelligence Agency, and monk Ironside VIII, who claims his tradition of celibacy dates back to Orpheus. I assured each of them that my research would be painstaking and that each would be informed of my conclusions simultaneously so that none would be given an unfair political advantage over the others.

Before my arrival a portion of the Orepheus' article in *Popular Electronics* had already been deciphered:

"According to Hunt's book, the original Bay of Pigs blueprint consisted of three parts. First, a Cuban expeditionary force would establish a beach head and 'government-in-arms'. Second, Radio Swan, transmitting from Swan Island 'and elsewhere' would broadcast appeals for help on behalf of the government-in-arms. Finally, with these widely heard Radio Swan broadcasts as justification, there would be massive Pentagon intervention. Someone, apparently the newly elected President John F. Kennedy, cancelled all but the first part of the plan".

Radio Swan of course was later known as Radio Americas (by the time of the Cuban missile crisis), while the Joint Chiefs of Staff made Swan Island off limits for archaeological research several centuries ago. On the other hand, areas around New York City are virtually no-man's land. I took three bottles of the Atlantis' gin with me.

I don't expect any major difficulties from either the CIA or Joint Chiefs. Both have long established power bases and thus should be able to ideologically adjust to whatever I might find. An entirely different situation exists with regards to monk Ironside's Church of the True America which has only in the past few years become a major power. His church believes "the United States of America was the beginning of the restoration of the Kingdom of God in the universe and was therefore cleansed of all things that offend and of them which is iniquity.....America will fill the universe with fruit!"

II—MONTAGE FOR VTR

(1)   A fuck
Some TV (Ironside)
That's it (grip her left buttock)
That's enough (Euridice)
"Love me?" ("You've lost a little weight off your bottom")
"No" (You'd like me even if I were skin and bones")
"Not even a little bit? I really sweated for that last 100 I gave you".
      "You got paid for it good, didn't you?"
"Yes"
      Some TV.... "The Comic Book Shortwave Caper"

(2)   I woke up in the Washington safe house with a splitting headache and half my memory gone. Now as we drive toward Long Island I can remember bits and pieces. "Euridice" (a code name of course) and I are part of a select Pentagon intelligence task force assigned to track down T.X. Thrush, supposedly a renegade CIA agent. The CIA and Pentagon have been rivals for over a decade

now but T.X. stopped taking orders from anybody in Washington circa 1965.

2.00 AM and Euridice has the speedometer up around 90. There are no cops in sight and our security clearance takes precedence over the energy crisis anyway. "How's your head?" The car radio has been converted for shortwave reception. She turns it up a little for the news from Radio Free Potomac.

(3)   Impeachment Debate

The first session, on the evening of July 24, was interrupted by a bomb threat which therefore permitted the insertion of commercials.

(Euridice is riding around in a red cadillac these days. It belongs to one of her other lovers, a small time soul DJ. She works as a stock girl at Dresses Inc. warehouse; once in a while, when they're short on sales people, in the store itself, the downtown store.)

The morning of July 25 began with a defense, by Charles Wiggins of California, of the President's CIA cover. By afternoon a clear Republican swing toward impeachment had surfaced. One of them refuted Nixon's CIA defense. At 3:38 the proceedings were interrupted by another bomb threat.

Last Saturday Euridice met
One of Gladys Knight's Pips

(4)   "About the same". I've had worse from a hangover. It's the memory thing that bugs me. I first tangled with T.X. back in August 1967 when he masterminded Reality Anonymous—a network of flea powered, unlicensed TV stations. But their range was so limited he switched to shortwave and broadcast soul music from a number of sites with interchangeable identities (Radio Hell, Radio Free Experimenter, Voice of Inner Earth and others). He switched their IDs around so fast it gave the impression they were in orbit. But he doesn't really have access to any space hardware. "How far are we from New York?"

"About another 100 miles to Jersey City". Euridice looks tired but we are to be on Long Island by noon and she doesn't think I'm ready to drive yet. "Why don't you get some sleep".

(5)   A second California Republican, Carlos Moorhead, came on like a soft sell evangelist; one expected him to break down and cry.

He supported the President. "I hope and pray that God guides this committee....".

In the evening a final swing vote declared for impeachment.

"Faced with indignation over the Stevenson-sabotaged Cuban fiasco, President Kennedy....rushed before Congress to appeal for forty more million dollars to finance a ten year program 'to beat the Russian Communists to the moon'....The realm over which man has authority to reign is the earth and nothing but the earth....The 'builders of the tower of Babel' wanted to leave the earth and 'reach onto heaven' (Genesis II). God confounded their presumptuous experiment and their tower was sent crashing down to earth"—California evangelist Dan Gilbert, shortly after the Bay of Pigs

(When Orpheus found Euridice in 1959, she was built like Gladys Knight)

(6)   "No, I just want to try and get my head together". I open the glove compartment and take out a flashlight and T.X.'s latest handiwork; subversive comics which he plans to distribute world-wide via shortwave facsimile broadcasting.

"Okay, maybe the drawings will bring it back to you. She switches the receiver over to facsimile, tunes to 3357 kHz, and it prints out the latest weather from NSS back at Washington. Somehow the subtly curving milibar lines always remind me of Euridice.

One of the comic strips which T.X. plans to broadcast via shortwave stars Wonder Woman burglarizing the White House for more of those Presidential tapes. Another shows her leading a raid on the ITT facsimile transmitters at Brentwood on Long Island. All of a sudden some of it does start to come back. "That's why we're headed for L.I. The military security was too tough at NSS so they're going to seize Brentwood instead". Brentwood is guarded only by a select group of FBI agents who secretly operate the station for the Pentagon.

(7)   But nothing counts unless you get paid for it

Shit, this ain't the wheel chair olympics.

"The secret ambition of a great many shortwave listeners is to single handedly uncover a piece of international intrigue. The radio waves themselves offer enormous opportunities to do just that. For example, beginning with a single piece of unusual trans-mission during the Cuban missile crisis, when Radio Americas switched IDs with VOA sites (including the historic one at

Brentwood, now of ITT SW facsimile fame) we determined that it was primarily a military, rather than a CIA, operation. We further learned that it was capable of transmitting from secret locations other than its publicized Swan Island site. Now these conclusions have been confirmed by none other than E. Howard Hunt of Watergate fame"—*Popular Electronics*, Oct. 1974

(But nothing counts unless you get paid for it)

(8)   "That's right." We slowed, pulled off into a service area for gas. "The raiding party rendezvous sometime tomorrow. Want some coffee?"

"Yes." I lay the drawings face down on the seat and kill the flash as the attendant appears.

"Fill it up." There is no one else waiting behind us so Euridice leaves the car and goes in for the coffee. I take mine black with a lot of sugar.

Another T.X. scenario has Wonder Woman emerging from Inner Earth in a space ship. Euridice is back. She pays the attendant, we pull ahead and drink our coffee in the dark. "Do you remember our part in the Brentwood operation?"

(9)   Hungate, a Democrat from Missouri, impersonated Jimmy Stewart's TV lawyer Hawkins. By the night of July 26 it became clear that the President's men, led by Sandman of New Jersey (a character from the Toma police series), had embarked upon a strategy of delay. This strategy apparently collapsed the next day. After which the conservative Democrats and liberal Republicans comandeered the Sandman tactic to cite the mass of evidence against Nixon.

(Shit, this ain't the wheel chair olympics)

(10)   "Not yet." The coffee is hot. Outside a little fog has begun to drift in from the ocean. "If that stuff gets any worse we're going to have problems."

"We know about half of the raiders on sight." On the highway again. "We are to cruise around Brentwood and try to spot one of them who will then lead the Pentagon to T.X. himself." Despite the fog we are back up to 90. "The Joint Chiefs don't want to put more security on ITT itself and scare them off." Back in 1967 when we were tracking down Reality Anonymous I can remember driving through another fog with Euridice. Just like a hoaky story in the old *Radio-TV Experimenter*.

16

(11)   About 5.10 Republican Hogan of Maryland (a former FBI agent) detailed Nixon's attempted use of the CIA as cover. In rebuttal, Wiggins cited again the former CIA personnel involved in the Watergate burglary. At 7.05 PM the first article of impeachment was approved.

(Euridice Williams, black, 40, muscular arms and thighs, putting on some weight around the middle.

"Get your ass over here, woman.")

(The Bay of Pigs has become the rosetta stone for anyone out to construct a clandestine theory of history. Every crackpot, every fanatic. . . .)

(12)   She has the facsimile telecopier on again and NSS is broadcasting something special—a composite drawing of T.X. Thrush which they have just been able to piece together. "Look familiar, honey?"

"Yeah". I pull the print off the machine and shine my flash light full on it. "I can almost place him."

"They must have got enough from the security force at NSS to put this together." We are through Jersey City now. Hoboken and the Holland Tunnel are just ahead. The commuter traffic hasn't started to build up yet.

"Think they'll issue this to the civilian police?"

My memory of Pentagon intelligence procedures is now pretty clear. "Not for a while anyway. They'd like to keep the publicity lid on if at all possible." The sun has just risen and we are driving into it. "After all T.X.'s whole purpose in seizing ITTBrentwood is to publicize shortwave facsimile."

(13)   Coverage by the commercial networks was technically superior to that provided by non-profit NPACT. But during NPACT coverage on the afternoon of July 29 a black woman, Barbara Jordan from Texas, subtly compared Nixon to a "mother". A little later the ranking Republican hinted at a secret national security aspect.

(The secret aspects of the Bay of Pigs culminated in Watergate)

(Euridice says she's not interested. "They've got their ·problems and I've got mine.")

As a result of the Kennedy assassinations, it was Nixon who got to conquer the Moon.

(14)   Another drawing casts Wonder Woman as a faith healer

putting a spell on the President's tape recorder. Euridice puts Radio Free Potomac back on which is playing some cuts from a Gladys Knight and the Pips album. "Keep looking at that drawing from NSS, honey, it may bring it all back to you."

By this time we are into heavy commuter traffic crawling along Eastern Parkway. And the fog is still with us. If anything it has gotten worse. "How is it we know what so many of the Thrush people look like?" I wish I had another cup of coffee.

"We've worked with some of them since 1967." The east bound traffic begins to thin out a little past Lynbrook. "All the way back to when you found one of Reality Anonymous' clandestine TV transmitters."

(15) At 9.25 General Haig was implicated. At 11.25 pm a second article of impeachment was voted against the President. At 3.29 on the afternoon of the 30th, but by a much smaller margin, a third article was approved.

Don Edwards, a Democrat from California, raised the Bay of Pigs matter, "an American invasion of Cuba", at 5.11.

("I don't want to hear that shit.")

(16) Atlantis, the lost continent, arises again from Inner Earth while Wonder Woman hovers overhead in her space ship. ITT Brentwood is after all beamed to ships at sea. Until the early 1960s the Voice of America operated from Brentwood but, officially, the VOA has no information on the disposition of that equipment.

"There was infiltration after that, wasn't there." The sun begins to burn away the fog. "Since 1967 we 've been able to function as double agents."

"That's part of it, honey." Euridice points toward another of those Thrush comic strips. It shows Wonder Woman's mate disguising himself as Howard Hunt. I start to remember the last piece of the puzzle as we swing off on the Sagtikos State Parkway which will take us to Brentwood.

(17) Beginning on the evening of August 8, Nixon turned his departure from the White House into an All American spectacular. Come morning he even wept on TV. With his family on camera, of course. In the end, he pictured himself as Theodore Roosevelt. This was by far Nixon's best TV performance. Around noon on the west coast there was a rally at the El Torro Marine Air Station which concluded with Nixon's supporters singing "God

Bless America."

(Hell, this is nut country—John F. Kennedy just before they shot him.)

"If I let you have the 100 dollars now instead at the end of the month would that help you out?"

(18)   I straighten up and lean toward Euridice so that I can see myself in the rear view mirror. Double check with that drawing from NSS then remember it all. I am the infamous Thrush myself. Have been ever since Euridice persuaded me to defect to Reality Anonymous while at the same time continuing to pose as a Pentagon operative. I blew my cover in Washington but tomorrow I will personally lead the raid on Brentwood's ITT/FBI shortwave facsimile broadcast station.

(19)   One evangelist, after watching a manned space ship blast off for the moon, said he knew that Christ was coming
again.

(Need a big assed woman to save my soul
Save my soul
Big assed mama let the good times roll)
(She takes off her dress
to turn him on
for 100 dollars)
Howard Hunt likes slender white blondes
Orpheus likes a round black mama
Fuck, woman, fuck
The fruit of this planet will survive
(Last Saturday Euridice met
One of Gladys Knight's Pips)

The Houston File

Back on Titan again. Days at the University, going through their archives—most of the stuff from Earth, much of it undated and of dubious origins. This file was recovered from a site, known as "November", on the northern shore of Lake Erie.

Nights drinking at the Atlantis. Fucking one of the barmaids.

[*Those reprinting this material should credit it both to T.X.' Thrush and the Arctic Short Wave Club*]

According to a New York Times *Service report in the XII/31* San Francisco Chronicle—*"E. Howard Hunt.... told the Senate Watergate Committee last year in still unpublished testimony that he served as the first chief of covert action for the Central Intelligence Agency's Domestic Operations Division..... Hunt.. Denied any involvement in or knowledge of spying on radicals and other dissidents by the Domestic Operations Division. But he added that some of his projects from the 1962-66 period—which dealt largely with the subsidization and manipulation of news and publishing organizations—did seem 'to violate the intent of the agency's charter'....Hunt.. told the Watergate Committee that the domestic operations division had 'established field operations in Boston and Chicago and San Francisco to name a few cities. These were parallel to the extant overt CIA establishment [already set up in these cities], and a large variety of domestic-based operations were conducted by this division. "*

(According to an unconfirmed report, circa 1975, a San Francisco missionary station which broadcast the WORD of GOD also had begun operations as Radio Americas LIBRE.)

I am back into the Gutenberg galaxy. For the moment my own 60th century exists not in time but in print. It is anti-matter. Which Heaven defines as any point in the space/energy/time continuum that does not conform to the Universal laws of physics. As for example the so-called black holes where, according to Jerry Pournelle writing in the Dec. 1974 *Galaxy*, we encounter infinite mass within the finite universe thus suspending the laws of physics.

Or the human psyche.

There is only one real Universe but any number of anti-matter alternates and, ultimately, these do in fact alter the real universe.

First it should be noted that, according to previous testimony before the Watergate Committee, Hunt was officially employed by the Dept. of Defense during the 1960-65 period. His connection with Radio Swan [later known as Radio Americas], and the military nature of this Bay of Pigs station, are now well established.

The following is from Newark News Radio Club's shortwave section of Nov. 1962 edited by Hank Bennett who at that time was also shortwave editor for Popular Electronics: *"Well, whatya know—Radio Americas has started in the QSL'ing business! Quite a few of our reporters have reminded me of this fact and I realized it myself, a couple of weeks ago. I received a most cordial letter from one of the people at the station. Perhaps some of you may remember back a few years when Yours Truly made a personal appearance on a BCB station [BCB yet!!], known as WKDN for a NNRC special. The d.j. at that time is none other than this fellow that is on Swan Island."*

The civilization around November was destroyed by anti-matter warfare circa 2280.

QSL letters for WKDN's 1953 NNRC DX test were signed by Robert Houston.

(WKDN-FM was later sold to a religious organization inter-connected with the San Francisco missionary station)

Some definitions:

DX—a form of escapism popular in the mid-20th century involving the reception of distant or rare electromagnetic radiation.

BCB—a range of electromagnetic frequencies normally used only for local or regional sound broadcasting (more correctly known as Medium Frequencies).

QSL—card, letter or other form of printed matter confirming DX reception. The Titan archives contain a Radio Swan QSL letter signed by "Horton H. Heath" (Howard Hunt?).

("I've got company right now. I'm taking care of some business.")

The following is from Bennett's April 1963 section:

"Several months ago this writer suggested that Radio Americas might be aboard a ship that was cruising in Caribbean and Atlantic waters. Subsequent information, including an in-person visit with a member of the Radio Americas staff, proved beyond a doubt that my original suggestion was quite in error. We

*were partially guided, as I mentioned at the time, that this belief
was due to the fact that an airline pilot who was reporting in to PE,
had found this ship by direction finder. Now we have a new report
from another PE monitor, a very capable gentleman, who claims
that Radio Libertad is actually the shipboard station.''*

Promises of tomorrow   (This is beginning to sound like
Black women   minor league Pynchon)
With naturals

(Another station reportedly operating as Radio Americas Libre
was Radio-TV Dominicana which uses facilities of the former Radio
Caribe, once mouthpiece for Trujillo, the butcher of Santo
Domingo. The CIA assassinated Trujillo. Could it be that people in
the Pentagon used the Trujillo family to organize the JFK killing as
an act of revenge?)

In late 1963 and early 1964 we received, as shortwave editor of
Electronics Illustrated, *three letters from Walter M. Giordano of
Natick, Mass. The first letter begins as follows—''I wrote a letter
to 'Feedback' several months ago concerning one of your articles
on Radio Americas. The letter was never published and for this I
am grateful as the letter was not very good. I know a little about
the letter the fellows at the station wrote you [which for some reason never reached us—TXT] and one of them told me it was just to
confuse you a little. From what I have seen, you are not the only
person who feels Radio Americas is not on Swan Island. I believed
it myself until I made a friend at the station. The reason I have
written to you now, was to see if you'd be interested in seeing
some photographs I have of the island and the station. I can also
tell you anything else you would like to know about the station,
antennas, owners, etc.''*

I have seen the streets of November
A thousand times   (''What's the matter?''
Once   ''I'm just busy now.'')

*From the next Giordano letter—''I have enclosed four letters
from a member of the Radio Americas staff. I hope you can find
plenty of information in them. As for the photographs I have some
very discouraging news. It seems the photos were not meant for
me to keep and I had to send them back. You will see for yourself in
letter no. 4. I can tell you what was in the photos and if I receive
any more I will send them to you before returning them. There
were several taken from the air showing the whole island. The
transmitters were housed in traliers. I believe all this information
is in the letters anyway.''*

25

From the final Giordano letter—"As for the number of an-tennas I saw in the photos, I think two or possibly three but I am really not sure. I thought there was some mention of the an-tennas in Mr. Houston's first letter. If there is any other infor-mation you would like to have let me know and I can always get the answer for you from Mr. Houston."

"In the U.S. 'Underground' comes to mean anti-Marketplace content but formwise is a very close shadowing of marketplace techniques. A hardsell (message) predominates. . . . Art at the ser-viceof the revolution and the revolution remains political, not metaphysical. . . . which is the *base* of the true *avant garde*. . . . Higgins is fascinated by—to quote Marineti—'the abstract a-log-ical synthesis of pure elements'. In other words the *artistic equivalent of a chance universe*. This is the key to Higgins' dis-satisfaction with 'traditional' forms. They are artificial points of *organization* in the midst of *natural disorganization*. He is inter-ested in disorganizing art." *Small Press Review* #21

But isn't an art of the "disorganized" merely another alternate to the real universe—another experiment in anti-matter which will automatically create an organization of its own? If Higgins is trying to disorganize all art, isn't he conceding an ultimate order? Nature is or is not organized: when one takes a fixed position on this, one automatically accepts a permanent state—a tangible relationship between anti-matter and reality.

The power people are becoming restless. The joint Chiefs of Staff, the CIA, Pope Ironside all want answers and I don't have any yet. I may have to shoot my own script and pass it off as the real thing.

Some dates:

April 1961—Bay of Pigs. Kennedy vetoes all-out Pentagon invasion of Cuba. Trujillo's Radio Caribe was apparently part of Pentagon plan.

May 1961—Kennedy permits CIA to assassinate Trujillo.

Oct/Nov. 1962—Cuban missile crisis. Kennedy still refuses to allow Pentagon invasion of Cuba.

Nov. 3, 1962—Radio Free Russia began broadcasting over slain Trujillo's Radio Caribe and Oswald had just returned from Russia to Dallas by way of Rotterdam where he'd rented an apartment.

Radio Free Russia announced its mailing address as a Rotterdam post office box. Oswald immediately became part of the anti-Communist White Russian community in Dallas.

Nov. 22, 1963—Oswald assassinates Kennedy.

("You knew I was going to get some of that extra money out of you, I'll bet you called me all kinds of black bitch.")

As E. Howard Hunt testified, one of the prime purposes of his covert domestic operations during this period was the manipulation of news and publishing organizations. And as noted in December, *vol. 15—"If these links are something more than a wildly improbable series of coincidences, then we have established a consistant, ongoing pattern of clandestine Pentagon involvement in both international broadcasting and this Thrush-like subculture for over a decade." But just how the CIA fits into this remains to be seen.* [*T.X. Thrush*]

I'd sell my soul	(In one creation myth, Purusha
For the truth	a giant spider secretes
Damn it.	an interminable thread
(Fuck it to me, mama	weaves a web
Nice and slow)	lives in it)

Another spring at monitoring station November.

Monitoring Station November

The Buffalo low frequency radio beacon is silent. Most of the other LF morse identities which marked out the cities and towns of the United States have also either left the air or will in the near future. Coming back to the band is a spooky experience—like the whole North American continent has been wiped out. But the weather broadcasts are still on and so are the Canadians.

[*they agreed to give him Euridice, but on one condition—Orpheus must go back to the world of light, followed by his mistress, without once turning around to look at her before he left the kingdom of the dead.*]

(The cameras and microphones are hidden.)

That's my cover, technician in charge of a Canadian LF beacon and weather broadcast station on the north shore of Lake Erie. I have the place to myself—installing the clandestine monitoring gear was no problem at all. And with most of the frequencies empty, I have a clear shot at Soviet signals coming across the pole.

There is something mystical about monitoring signals from the depths of the radio spectrum—going further and further into the lower frequencies, into the Earth-ionosphere cavity—something sexual. But my assignment is the trans-polar depths.

Although the operation here is clandestine, its classification is not very high. "November" is one of a dozen Canadian ionospheric monitoring stations operated by the Technological Intelligence Agency. If one of these monitoring posts is compromised, another could be readily set up to take its place. I am considered a security risk and this is the end of the TIA line for me. All I do here is collect the raw data and feed it back to Wasington where it is processed by a TIA computer in the Pentagon. They cannot dispense with me or my services entirely. I may have cached notes (these that you are reading) which would surface if I were to disappear.

Man-made radio began on these inner frequencies—back in the spark gap era.

[*Big assed mama let the good times roll*

31

Let the good times roll.
Need a big assed mama to save my soul]

All my previous assignments were tropical—in the Dominican Republic at one of the Pentagon's alternate Bay of Pigs broadcast sites, at an experimental short wave radar station on Swan Island (the original Swan Island transmitter was built by United Fruit circa 1912), in the Arizona desert where we tested a new high powered portable medium wave unit (1963) and some portable TV stations in 1966. The circuit which joins these sites creates a logic of its own, is beyond the laws of time and place, stretches on through Canada and into a void which I no longer understand.

At this point I cannot even be absolutely certain that there is such a thing as the Technological Intelligence Agency or, if the TIA does exist, whether I am actually working for it. Agencies within the Pentagon frequently exchange identities. As do the operatives who work for them. For example, the hero of E. Howard Hunt's "The Venus Probe" assumes the alias Roberto Hughes, which is very close to Robert Houston—an employee of the Pentagon's Radio Americas: the latter known as Radio Swan and Radio Escambre Libre during the Bay of Pigs operation with which Hunt was connected. But was that the real Robert Houston? I used the Houston alias while at Santo Domingo (or Ciudad Trujillo as it was known in those days) and am using it again here in Canada (while Hunt is out on bail pending appeal of his Watergate conviction).

I met Euridice in 1959 while I was stationed at the Brentwood [Long Island] field office. I picked her up at Jack's Bar & Grill on Pine street which at that time was the black red-light district. Later on, when I started making the big money, I set her up in a flat in Buffalo [Hunt's hometown]. Right from the beginning Euridice had class, a real major league woman. And I was a major league agent in those days too.

The TIA has been experimentally altering the polar ionosphere. They hope eventually to be able to enhance or wipe out radio reception at will. This in turn relates to their experiments with short wave radar and psychological warfare. The relatively clear frequencies in the earth-ionosphere cavity provide the best oportunity for verifying these alterations.

Euridice has hustled on the street, one arrest, no conviction.

Occasionally I pick up weather broadcasts from Long Island on 418 khz. It was my interest in Long Island weather broadcasts, the visual ones on short wave, which led to my classification as a security risk.

"Shortwave facsimile broadcasting has been around for quite a while. It has been used by the Navy and other government agencies to broadcast weather charts and similar graphic material, but only recently has equipment been available to the general public for its reception. . . . watch for ITT's facsimile broadcasts from Brentwood, Long Island, at 1450 to 1650 EST on 17,436.5 khz (WFK67). Brentwood was formerly the location of a Voice of America transmitter"— *Popular Electronics,* Dec. 1973

I was responsible for leaking the material that went into the PE article. I still don't understand the TIA's reaction to it. When there are no Russians in the earth-ionosphere cavity, and I am not contemplating my one weekend a month with Euridice, I brood over Brentwood.

I have rented an old farm house where we meet secretly. It isn't safe for Euridice and me to be seen together. TIA personnel aren't supposed to have permanent connections, and sometimes I wonder why Euridice bothers: I can't give her the kind of money I used to.

"One of these days I'm going to make my move." Euridice is drinking vodka these days. "I'm disgusted with the whole thing, nigger."

A beacon from the Canadian arctic has appeared on 351 khz. I am alert for trans-polar signals in the earth-ionosphere cavity. But this may be one of the nights they have knocked out everything north of James Bay. Or is it really everything south of Lake Erie? When I first got into low frequency listening back in the early 50s the arctic beacons were always buried by signals from the U.S. I was a loner even then—just out of high school and looking for a way into the big money. Later I moved on to short wave broadcasting and the TIA.

(Nixon has just changed his story again.)

You'll just have to take my word for it—I am a TIA agent.

My first short wave job was editing a program for electronic hobbyists. The real assignment was to suppress any report of rare radio reception which might shed light on Pentagon operations. I took my orders from an agent calling himself Robert Houston. I never saw Houston after he moved on to Radio Americas so I don't know whether it was the same guy. Anyway Houston recommended that I be taken on as a full time operative and I moved on to the Dominican Republic site. The last broadcast I did from the U.S. featured a story on how the Voice of America would be gradually phasing out its Brentwood facility (then known as WDSI) over the next few years. Just before it was finally phased out of the VOA network, WDSI switched identities with Radio Americas during the Cuban missile crisis. Of course there would never have been a missile crisis had Kennedy permitted the Pentagon to carry out all of its Bay of Pigs plan.

(Major league woman, minor league man
Minor league man
Love her when you can]

("speculation on global weather interconnections, usually linked to the sunspot count, date back at least to beginning of international communication by radio. In fact, an extensive article on the subject appeared as early as the July 1927 'Science and Invention' magazine......Whether or not the sunspot count has a practical effect on the weather, it definitely affects the ionosphere"— —*Popular Electronics*, Dec. 1973)

Around 5.00 every afternoon I drive into town and call Euridice from a pay phone. "What are you doing?"

"Trying to get some sleep. But I've still got company."

"They haven't been there all weekend have they?" It's Sunday.

"No, just for the afternoon." Her voice is African velvet. She's had just enough to drink.

"You going to be able to make it into work tomorrow?"

"Maybe I will and maybe I won't."

Sometimes I have a nightmare in which Euridice's phone has been disconnected. I cannot get through to her. All the lines are out of order.

("How well can you get your receiver to print those millibars and other weather patterns that are broadcast?"—PE, Dec. 73)

In charge of the Santo Domingo transmitter site was an agent calling himself Hunt Roberts. He'd written a thesis on weather modification through ionospheric alteration and was awaiting transfer to USAF's Cambridge Research Labs. Shortly after I moved on to the Swan Island radar installation, I heard that his thesis had been accepted.

Euridice's place is a haven for loners and misfits like me.

A low pressure mandala has formed over James Bay matching a second over Leningrad. The outer rings of the disturbance have reached November and it has begun to snow. Roberts was always talking about mandalas. He said they represented both unity and the female—as do the great circle paths followed by radio signals. But the weather mandalas which occur naturally are always imperfect. At the time I was working with Roberts, I suspected his thesis had more to do with psychological warfare than any real attempt to alter the environment. Make those TV weather maps contain signs and portents; you could really scare the hell out of the suckers.

(But shortwave facsimile broadcasts to ships and aircraft would have to show the real thing, wouldn't they?)

"What are you doing?"

"Washing." Euridice is working these days as a stock girl at Dresses, Inc.

"You sound a little down."

"I'm just tired."

Swan Island, as it turned out, was on the great circle path which runs through Cambridge Research Labs and Cape Canaveral. That made it the perfect location for an experimental short wave radar installation with the Bay of Pigs propaganda operation providing a ready made cover for our experiments. So the Cuban debacle served some purpose after all—even though Kennedy did screw it up. The men on Swan were all Nixon loyalists. After the assassination there was a wild celebration. Most of us stayed drunk for a week.

(Kennedy and Nixon; voices on the radio, faces on the TV, props for the TIA's scenario like the weather, the ionosphere, missiles and mandalas)

November is across the highway from a cemetery. Today it seemed like there was one continuous funeral.

"Why don't you fix yourself a drink."

"I've still got some of your vodka left."

"It'll settle you down."

"No, I want to wait until I see you next weekend. When I drink I want to do a good job of it."

Right after the missile crisis I was transferred to Arizona for those portable field tests. On Swan we all figured Kennedy would be forced into a Cuban invasion to get those Soviet missiles. But it didn't work out that way. When I left Swan they were talking about more power for the radar experiments.

Signals from the Mont Joli beacon have appeared at November. Mont Joli is a final reporting point for aircraft on the North Atlantic great circle route.

[Euridice's maroon tits and mahogany buttocks are mandalas]

The Arctic mandala is intersected by a myriad of others, those great circles on the shortwave facsimile weather charts: all frozen,

35

all being imperceptibly altered by the TIA toward a new perfection. It was during the Swan experiments that the Pentagon first discovered the effects of super powered short wave signals on the ionosphere but as of the last intelligence report I saw at Brentwood, a practical system for ionospheric alteration still existed only on paper. A pilot film for the ultimate TV series.

(The TIA brass are being especially cautious because of the Watergate scandal. Except for routine monitoring, such as the operation here at November, all the research projects are in a state of suspension.)

Just before publication of the PE article, I was assigned to a special assassination contingency unit as a result of my participation in the Arizona portable field tests. One of the unit's functions is to set up an alternate broadcast system in the event of Nixon's removal from office.

Euridice always rides
Naked woman flesh
Once in a plaid beret

[*Before joining the TIA, I wanted to become a writer. I told an editor I was a corrupt freudist—I saw everything as a battle between death and sex.*]

[*At least I write as well as Howard Hunt.*]

After the *Popular Electronics* piece appeared, I was suspected of, among other things, working for the Pentagon's arch enemy, the Central Intelligence Agency. If Nixon is assassinated, the CIA will be blamed for it even though the Pentagon would now benefit most from his death. Better a dead martyr than a live crook. It scares Euridice when I tell her Nixon will probably have to be killed.

My replacement here at November for that one weekend a month, who calls himself Howard Heath, was in Dallas when Kennedy got it. He is the only one ever to hear a Russian low frequency broadcast at this monitoring site. He also once proposed the use of shortwave facsimile for the transmission of hardcore pornography into the Soviet Union. As he put it "Pornography is power". Before the TIA recruited him, Heath was Brentwood's one man vice squad.

"Don't call me tomorrow night. I'm going out right after work, Call me Sunday afternoon."

For the first time I have been able to log a low freqency beacon on the fringe of the Arctic Circle herself, beyond James and even Hudson's Bay, where patches of scrub evergreen give way to endless white. A mandala defined, with almost perfect symmetry by the orbit of our planet around that star we call the Sun. Someday the mandalas on the weather chart will match the Arctic Circle's perfection. As soon as the Pentagon disposes of Watergate.

When I did this for a hobby, I used to hear beacons on the tropic circles. So far reception of these has been completely wiped out here at November. Euridice and I will rendezvous at the farm house around noon this coming Saturday.

Some more mythology. They showed the movie "Z" tonight on television. That's the one about the events which led up to the military takeover in Greece. TIA people speculate that the film was actually made by the Central Intelligence Agency. Certainly its showing on network TV at this time is going to make things just that much tougher for Nixon.

One Saturday night I took Euridice to the local bar. They had brought in a black exotic from across the border but most of the Canadians were more interested in a hockey game on TV. She got the fuck out of there as soon as she could. The TIA brass knew what they were doing when they picked November for a monitoring station.

(The circuit creates its own logic.)

Afterwards some hillbilly music on the jukebox;

Walk on by

Wait on the corner

We're strangers when we meet

A couple weeks after they shot Kennedy they gave me leave and I spent it with Euridice. Neither of us could really believe that a president of the United States would be assassinated.

During the spring of 1972 there were torrential rains and floods in the U.S. and a few of those weather charts contained some pretty weird patterns. There was speculation amongst low echelon TIA men that our experimental alterations of the ionosphere might have got out of hand—particularly the installation at Orfordness in England. Orfordness is on or close to a great circle running through two major Soviet missile sites. We used to call it the Swan Island of Europe. The British government shutdown that operation about the same time Watergate began to break.

(Howard Hunt has an almost pathological hatred for the British.)

Wednesday morning there is what Hunt Roberts would call a threat of spring at November and this evening the static level has increased noticeably. There will be no chance of picking up weak signals from the Arctic. Unless of course the TIA experiments have progressed much further than is generally believed. If they could substantially wipe out radio signals from south of the Great Lakes that would also eliminate most of the static.

Static is the primordial radio signal. The earth-ionosphere cavity was filled with it long before man built his first transmitter.

[*Pornography is power''*]

(Could it be that the PE article created an alternate script—a heresy to the TIA's scenario?)

Heath always arrives sharp at 6.00 the night before I leave. He brings with him a batch of *Playboys*, *Penthouses* and *Ouis*. His favorite picture is one of Hitler spanking a bare female ass. They display no marks of course but there is a subtle pattern on her buttocks that resembles those curving milibar lines on the facsimile weather charts.

The static has become even heavier by the time he arrives but he hints this will be corrected over the weekend. Sometimes I think his claims of spectacular trans-polar reception are phony but on my way to meet Euridice I really don't give a shit about the Arctic circle.

Euridice is putting on a little weight these days. She says she only drinks on weekends.

Nixon has chiseled about half a million dollars on his taxes.

Tropic circles.

"I've been drinking and I'm evil so don't fuck with me."

"Do you remember me calling last night?"

"No." She hunted through her purse for a pack of matches. "What did you call for, you knew you were going to see me today anyway."

"I just wanted to make sure your ride was set." We both arrived at the farm house before noon. I gave the guy who drove her a ten and he will be back for Euridice Sunday afternoon. We have already worked our way through one bottle and into Saturday evening.

According to Howard Hunt, then vice-president Nixon was the Bay of Pigs action officer within the White House. That of course was before he lost the election to Kennedy. A fluke of history? Like the bungled Watergate burglary, and the story I leaked to *Popular Electronics* so I could give Euridice a few more dollars. Accidents of history or a counter-conspiracy?

Euridice Williams—raised by her great aunt and uncle until he ran off to Chicago with another woman and Euridice went back to the bottom of nigger hill. He shot his mistress in Chicago then himself and made it into JET. "Watch out, nigger, I've been drinking and I'm evil."

Outside a freak March thunderstorm is moving in from the northwest. Monitoring at November must be completely wiped out. I haven't seen lightning like this since I left the tropics. Even the local TV stations are becoming difficult to watch.

(I am not now, nor have I ever been, a plant for the Central Intelligence Agency.)

"Let's put some music on." She turns off the Television. If they kill Nixon tonight I won't know it til morning.

"You still scared of thunder and lightning?"

"Shit, I just want to hear some music."

(Giant cyclonic storms are sweeping across the Midwest.)

Watch the cops prowl the street, make it shake. Euridice pours us each another drink.

Big assed mama, let the good times roll.

Let the good times roll

Need a big assed mama to save my soul

When I left November I made damn sure I wasn't followed. That's why I moved Euridice out of Brentwood in the first place: I didn't want them to know where she was. And maybe a hiding place for me someday—if things really get hot after they dispose of Nixon.

[*"One of these days I'm going to make my move."*]

(The Cambridge Research Laboratories claim to have never heard of Howard Heath even though he presently describes himself as the USAF's foremost low frequency researcher.)

We have furnished only two rooms in the farm house: the kitchen and this one. Euridice lies back on the bed. "Don't get no funny ideas."

"Why not?"

"I'll let you know when I'm ready to take care of business." With the rest of the house empty, the whole thing is a little like a set from* Mission Impossible. *Bed, hifi, table, liquor—just enough props for the sex scene. But then my whole career sounds like something out of* The Man From UNCLE, *or one of Howard Hunt's spy novels.*

(The cameras and microphones are hidden.)

I have a real high on now and decide that the first thing Monday morning I will begin another article for *Popular Elec-*

tronics—about Radio Swan, Santo Domingo, and the Bay of Pigs. "What Hunt doesn't tell us is that at 2300 EST the next night a 'Radio Escambre Libre' appeared on 7000 khz with anti-Castro slogans and fictitious orders to those same fictitious guerillas."

"I pulled a muscle in my thigh at work last week so be careful." She is naked from the waist down.

"Want me to massage it?"

"No, just fuck and get it over with."

The storm has moved off to the east slightly and must now be directly over the monitoring station.

Nixon hated the Kennedys because they could still make out. Oswald was supposed to have shot them both. For a TIA man, everything is missiles and mandalas. "Pornography is power." The circuit creates its own logic.

"Which thigh did you pull the muscle in."

"The right."

I give her a spank on the left buttock.

"Mother fucker."

(These notes will alter the circuit. The article I begin on Monday will re-arrange the props)

Naked.......... Radio Swan, Escambre Libre, Americas

Woman.......... Electronic voices

Flesh.......... From nowhere

"One of these days I'll have something good going for me and I'm going to make my move." When the games are over and we really get it on Euridice always rides. ("Make up a reference log of any station that falls on or very near that great circle which includes you, Cape Kennedy and the transmitter"—*Popular Electronics*

Orpheus and Euridice	*She stands*
Screwing	*Naked black*
Eternity	*Woman myth*
If I get to write the script	*Becomes flesh*

"One of these days I'm going to make my move, nigger."

[FADE]

Interface: 29 Scenes from the Late Show

#1   By the year 2001 the surface of this planet will have become Inner Earth City, divided into tribally oriented mini-states, and surrounded by a myriad of broadcast and communications satellites creating an Illusionary Television Universe controlled by a secret government on the Moon.

Wolfman dissolves into Marshall McLuhan disguised as Count Dracula masquerading as Sherlock Holmes played by Adolph Hitler.

#2   *In 1971 T.X. Ironside, illegitimate son of the famed paraplegic Television detective, had it made as a hack magazine columnist specializing in broadcast scandals.*

From an expose on radio evangelism he made enough to send his mistress, Euridice Williams, to Cape Kennedy for a week. Besides drinking on the beach, she was to bring back some pictures for him—nothing classified but they would make good background illustrations for his next hatchet job on the Voice of America.

#3   "No one would expect the VOA to braodcast everything about the space voyage, but when it reduces its schedule suddenly when something goes amiss, you know that all it is trying to protect is the nation's image. When the men of Apollo 13 were facing dire consequences, the news of it was scarce on VOA. Perhaps the mere fact that VOA has dropped 24 hour coverage of the event will be a good indication if anything is wrong."

Electronics Illustrated, March 1971

#4   In 2001 two domed cities on the Moon represent each of the major contending factions within the ITU. Nova Cathay is the stronghold of those favoring direct broadcast satellites while those supporting cable systems fed by communications satellites made their headquarters atop Mount McLuhan. The two groups compete for power through simulated adventures in outer space.

#5   *She sat on the edge of the couch and finished peeling off her panty hose. Euridice has a big belly, her thighs are braod and muscular. When she bent over Ironside to make love, Euridice looked like a lady Buddha. But she screws a hell of a lot better than any of those skinny broads you see on Television.*

43

#6   Throughout all of June and July (2001) a TV war was staged for possession of Saturn's largest moon, Titan. While this was in progress Wolfman exterminated an entire black tribe just south of Cape Kennedy but no one noticed.

#7   Euridice Williams, black, 38, a stock girl for Dresses Inc. On the night she came over to get the money for her trip to the cape she wore a yellow sweater, dark slacks and her African hair piece.

She said the traffic coming out of the city and over the bridge to Canada was heavier than usual.

#8   "Titania had long red hair, a 36-24-36 figure and looked like a human except that she was almost transparent. Titania was a real looker if you dig spooks. She nodded and five of her 'men' (who looked to be 100% human) boarded our saucer and went straight to that compartment where my giant radio towers were kept."

From a *Radio-TV Experimenter* short story

#9   Ironside envisions himself as a myth—a legendary high priest of Inner Earth City saving it from space hoaxes.

("Just think what would happen on election day '72 if a powerful TV signal appeared over various American communities via a secret satellite in polar orbit, claiming to be from an alien space ship, and ordering Americans to vote for a certain candidate or face extermination! Sure this *sounds* like science fiction. Just remember that unlike most sci-fi themes, it *could* happen."

Elementary Electronics, July-August 1970)

#10   He found Euridice hustling at Jack's Bar & Grill on Pine Street. That was around the time of the Cuban missile crisis. They had both come a long way since 1962.

#11   During the missile crisis all international broadcast identities controlled by the United States were interchangeable; they moved from one set of antenna towers to another at the speed of light. Only a few months earlier Washington had announced plans to send man to the Moon.

#12   Neither of the lunar cities are self sufficient. In fact each is totally dependent upon Inner Earth for survival. Any tribe which doesn't in some manner contribute to the support of Nova Cathay or Mount McLuhan is liquidated in the interests of slum clearance.

("McLuhan himself envisions an apartheid style world with integration taking place only at the cultural exchange level, if at all. . . .The individual will not receive pictures and sound directly off the air but by cable. Direct reception might permit members of one tribe to receive programming intended for another thus casting doubt upon the validity of that electronic reconstruction of the world provided by their own tribal chieftain."

Small Press Review #6-7)

#13   During the war for Titan, Nova Cathay's direct broadcast satellites claimed to be transmitting from the moon of Saturn itself. McLuhan's safer cable systems could never achieve this level of psychological impact.

("Should voice transmissions by the astronaut be monitored by short wave listeners throughout the world—listeners not familiar with the mission, flight plan, procedures etc.—many erroneous conclusions might be drawn and given wide circulation. Such a possibility could conceivably influence the astronaut's reporting of his reactions and observations."

NASA Public Affairs Office, 1962)

#14   Ironside, like McLuhan, is a Canadian. Despite its reputation for liberalism, Canada is basically a racist nation. But Ironside, unlike McLuhan, will always be an outsider anyway. A man in a wheel chair is expected to settle for any woman he can get.

"I wonder who you would've married if you weren't the way you are." Euridice poured them each another drink.

Radio Canada International recently began sharing a Portuguese antenna site with the Voice of Germany.

#15   Adolph Hitler is the prince of Nova Cathay. The first direct broadcast satellite was launched by the Communist Chinese in 1970. Unknown to Chairman Mao that project was secretly headed by Hitler's cousin, Count Dracula. In January 2001 Nova Cathay began experimenting with direct broadcasts from the moon itself. These transmissions were promptly jammed by the McLuhanists. As a result of this development in the media war, larger power supplies are needed by both sides and crash programs of nuclear reactor construction have been initiated in various Inner Earth mini-states.

Meanwhile certain members of that black tribe near the Cape, a McLuhanist colony, were suspected of watching Nova Cathay broadcasts from the Moon (reruns of "Mein Kampf") on a 1970 TV set which someone had unearthed. This explains the tribe's extermination.

"*The City* no longer exists, except as a cultural ghost for tourists."

#16   Since most of the stations on UHF are not affiliated with any network, the DX-equipped viewer has a much wider choice of news, musical, sports, religious and special programs than does his VHF counterpart. UHF viewers soon learn that difference is

*the rule in UHF programming, with films from antiquity, and
original low-budget productions accounting for some of the more
enjoyable moments."*   *EI, Sept. 1971*

*He got his start writing articles on how to hear distant ["DX"]
short wave stations. While Euridice was flying to Cape Kennedy
he spent the evening watching "Mein Kampf" which is high-
lighted by a panorama of naked women as they are marched into
the gas ovens.*

#17   EI's WIN-THE-WORLD CONTEST!

"Where in the world would you like to go? Paris? Moscow?
Aukland? Take the Grand Prize in EI's Win-the-World Contest and
we'll fly you there and back! To win the trip of a lifetime or any one
of 99 other valuable prizes all you have to do is practice your
favorite hobby—radio. Ours is a DX contest in which you count up
your QSLs to win. It's that simple!''.

#18   The next evening Ironside's UHF brought forth Sherlock
Holmes vs. "The Voice of Terror"—a fictitious Nazi short wave
station. Holmes' curtain line is something about a menacing East
wind.

"Sherlock Holmes is so much the type of intuitive genius it is
unnecessary to dwell at length on the characteristics of the intuitive mind. It is a mind for which situations are total and inclusive
unities. Every facet, every item of a situation, for Holmes, has
total relevance."

Marshall McLuhan, *Explorations #8*
(Sherlock Holmes is in reality related to the Ironside family by
marriage.)

#19   *ALL OF THESE SCENES ARE HATCHET JOBS,
PRODUCED BY INNER EARTH STUDIOS, AND DESIGNED TO
DISCREDIT THE ITU. Unlike his TV father, this Ironside has
never settled for second best. First he went out and got the kind of
woman he wanted. Now he plans to make it into the big time with
an all out assault on the Voice of America and its moon cult.*

#20   Wolfman is the tribal chieftain of Mount McLuhan. On the
Moon he is of course a beast 7 days a week, 52 weeks a year, with
no periods of remorse in between.

"The age of automation may well be not the age of the con-
sumer but of mystic contemplation."   Marshall McLuhan,
Explorations #8

#21   *Pay the rent then love me good
Love me good
If you didn't another man would*

Euridice is back from the Cape.

#22   Most werewolf movies are set in Europe but in point of fact this species was originally found only in the Canadian north woods. Ironside has a feeling sometimes that the beast is stalking him.

IRONSIDE FOR MAYOR   (another Inner Earth Production)

"It's said that a good man is hard to find. We'll politely say that a man more qualified than T.X. Ironside would be impossible to find. T.X. *has* to know about DX because he makes his living as a DXer. Thumb through any electronics magazine and you're sure to find many DXing articles with the world-famous Ironside byline. T.X.'s accomplishments in his 20 years of DXing have been nothing short of amazing. He has 111 countries verified, including every continent."

#23   *Euridice had stripped everything off but the sweater which would've messed up her hair. She rolled the sweater up around her shoulders.*

Ironside has a thing about cities. Flesh vs. a labrynth of steel, a little closer to his listening post. He hopes it engulfs him before the moon cult seizes power.

Euridice Williams, Born Oct. 28, 1932. Raised by her great aunt and uncle—until he left with another woman for Chicago. Educated in all negro public and high schools. First sex at 13. Graduated second in her class. Has hustled on the street, in a bar. One arrest.

#24   THE CANADIAN CRISIS

"A month after my column on the Canadian threat to jam the air waves and the international issue of listening freedom hit the stands, the Ottawa government with terrorist activity as justification (or excuse, depending upon which side of the debate you're on) assumed dictatorial powers, including arbitrary control over the broadcast media. Those powers have been used with great restraint—little has been directly censored by the government. Or more precisely, Canadian mass media has been used to circulate many wild tales, primarily intended to further justify the government's drastic action".

#25   *At the time of the 1970-71 Canadian crisis, McLuhan was posing as Ottawa's court jester.*

In 1975 Wolfman will be appointed as head of the Voice of America.

Euridice brought back pictures of white tourists on the beach watching the APOLLO 15 rocket blast off.

47

#26 "Private broadcasters have also engaged in some self-censorship. For example, Canada's second television network, CTV, cancelled a two-part Ironside adventure which depicted the framing of a secessionist cell."

Short wave listeners reporting reception from those Radio Canada International antenna towers shared with the Voice of Germany were sent in return an icon ("QSL") depicting Canada's first communications satellite which will be launched in 1972.

#27 *Except for Euridice and Inner Earth City, all the identities are interchangeable. Wolfman dissolves into Marshall McLuhan disguised as Count Dracula masquerading as Sherlock Holmes played by Adolph Hitler.*

#28 By the year 2001 the surface of this planet will have become Inner Earth City, divided into tribally oriented mini-states, and surrounded by a myriad of broadcast and communications satellites creating an Illusionary Television Universe controlled by a secret government on the Moon.

And the city
Inner Earth
Engulfed him
"Screw, woman, screw."

FADE

Notes From The Kalahari

[1] I'm a soldier of fortune by temperament, a radio technician by profession, and a genius at both. Which means that any place in the world someone wants to operate a propaganda station, chances are I'll apply for the job. So when this Rhodesian thing came up at the end of 65, I signed on with the KIA (Kalahari Intelligence Agency). The money was good and so were my references—chief radio aboard the Voice of America's top secret clandestine network during the Cuban missile crisis then later I was an adviser to the red Chinese while they set up a high powered relay in Tibet (both KIA projects incidentally). If there's a buck in it, they can trust me to do the job and keep my mouth shut.

I've been running all my life, ever since I took off from the Henley Institute for homeless boys—with its gray dormitories and clockwork routine. Running to prove I belong loose on this Earth, that I'm a man, that I can do anything any other man can do, and do it better. Running to stay out of Henley. Sometimes I dream I'm back in the dormitory again—but I'm getting out tomorrow. Then it is tomorrow, I wake up, and run some more.

KIA headquarters is a marble white castle atop Dracula's Mountain, at the edge of the Desert. Don't look for Dracula's Mountain on a map because you won't find it. But we're in Southwest Africa, just across the border from Botswana. In charge of the facility is Dr. Frankenstein who also carries on Astrological research in the castle.

A few nights after I arrived, I dreamed that Dr. Frankenstein had built me in a sub-cellar beneath the Henley Institute, next to the furnace room where it was very hot, like the Kalahari, and I woke up choking.

The KIA has operated from Dracula's Mountain since 1933 but Rhodesia was the first time that action had come this close to home. Dr. Frankenstein personally assumed control of all operations. He secretly borrowed portable equipment from Washington and set up the anti-Rhodesian station at Francistown, Botswana. Then he requisitioned some high powered transmitters

51

from Johannesburg and used them as jammers in Rhodesia against the Botswana station. I acted as his liaison man.

Until 1964 the whole of Southern Africa was governed by CFAP (Council for Fascism and Astrological Progress) with headquarters at Johannesburg and Heinrick Verwoerd as its High Priest. But in early 1965 another order, the League for Racial and Spiritual Purityi (LRSP) was granted permission to establish missions in Botswana (then Bechuanaland) and very shortly they demanded complete jurisdiction over neighboring Rhodesia. By November the ideological battle had become so intense that, in order to prevent a possible world war, the KIA found it necessary to take over and channel all propaganda aimed at inciting the masses, both black and white, until CFAP and LRSP could agree on an equitable compromise.

The League for Racial and Spiritual Purity has its headquarters in the United States, at Michigantown, in fact only a few blocks from the Henley Institute which they operate. LRSP's High Priest is Count Guano who, like CFAP's Herr Verwoerd, is a vampire.

The first thing I did when I got out of Henley was find myself a woman, a real tough, hard woman, the kind that would have been strictly off limits at Henley, the kind that it would take a real man to hold, the kind that would mark me as for real. I met Dice in front of Jack's Bar & Grill, on the corner of Pine and Illinois in Michigantown's lower harlem, with slum clearance across the street and cinders blowing in our faces. The rubble is still there, and so is Jack's.

As his liaison man (I travelled between the castle and transmitter sites by flying saucer) Dr. Frankenstein got to know me pretty well or so he thought. Frankenstein said I had superior powers, despite my Henley background. He began to confide in me. The Doctor considered both CFAP and LRSP as bunglers in his field—Astrology. He contended that the only useful purpose each served was to control the masses under their respective jurisdictions.

I set Dice up in a flat on Illinois Avenue and I lived there with her between jobs. We fixed the place up pretty freak, just the way she wanted it—a pearl gray bar in the corner with silver crescent moons on it, white wall to wall carpet, even a TV set with the picture tube on a swivel. When I was off we'd sleep till noon most days and then get ourselves together with coffee royal.

During the Rhodesia job, I got leave and back to her once a month. When I'm living with Dice, I don't dream much.

Dr. Frankenstein even let me read some of his basic texts on Astrology:

"A vision. Stars, planets, galaxies, the Universe expanding to its outer limits, then the whole astral system begins to collapse upon itself. Each billion years the night sky becomes a little brighter until the end when it explodes and everything is fire. Only the droppings of the deific intergalactic bats survive. From which, according to the laws of cause and affect, the cycle repeats exactly as it was before, the Universe expands towards its outer limits, we each live again, according to the laws of cause and effect, exactly as it was before—forever."

I started out at Jack's drinking gin but Dice switched me over to scotch. After that we always drank her brand—Johnny Walker red.

"One complete cycle takes 82 billion Earth years or so, in more scientific terms, 77,000 life spans of the intergalactic bat, in other words 77,000 IGBs during which there numerous subcycles."

(Both Guano and Verwoerd sprouted from droppings left when an IGB last visited this planet—in 1889).

"Dice has real class—and that's expensive. But while I'm working for the KIA, I don't have any trouble paying her bills.

"After that great fire which has destroyed all but the IGB droppings, we perceive the divine focus, from which emanate all intergalactic bats, as the spiritual center of the Universe, the pure white body of the formless one. But the time approaches when its mission in the scheme of creation must commence, according to the laws of cause and effect. The moment arrives, and as soon as the first creative pulsations of thought vibrate, the whole sphere of motionless, formless, white IGB droppings flashes forth sparkling with energy. And now, behold what a change has taken place. The soft white IGB droppings have ceased to be and in their place is raying forth in every conceivable direction mighty flocks of intergalactic bats. the cycle begins again!"

We'd seen all the late movies. Dice killed the TV, turned on the radio and got some blues from the local negro FM station WBLK.

Pay the rent then love me good.

Love me good.

If you didn't another man would.

[2] Dr. Frankenstein summoned Count Guano, Herr Verwoerd and their aids (including Verwoerd's protege Herr Worster) together for a peace conference at his castle early in 1966. The Doctor and Verwoerd were old friends. Frankenstein had built several

androids in his likeness. They appeared for the prime minister during daylight hours (when vampires are confined to their coffins) and at all public functions which considerably reduced the risk of assassination.

The night before that conference I dreamed I walked up a hill in Michigantown. The buildings, the street were all shades of light brown. Up that hill past a tenement with small square carefully regulated windows, little colored boys in each looking out at me. And at the top of the hill, I asked a white neighbor woman, middle aged derelict, for Dice. I hadn't seen her in a couple years and had lost her address. We couldn't use Dice's flat but the neighbor let Dice use her apartment to entertain me, her apartment at the top of the hill and Dice wore a green dress. Cheap summer cotton which clung nicely to the curve of her buttocks.

The peace conference opened with an official ceremony in the castle's hall of Astrological worship. Verwoerd, Worster and the other CFAP priests entered from the left draped in red robes. From the right came Count Guano and his LRSP priests draped in gold. At that great altar in the center of the hall stood Dr. Frankenstein and his sister, Titania, the white hag in my dream, arrayed in silver. They beheaded three African women in honor of the next intergalactic bat due to visit this planet in late 1974.

Oh, mighty IGB.

Giver of life.

Expander of the Universe.

Fertilizer of the divine spirit.

Bless us this day.

I arrived back in Michigantown from the Tibet job on a Monday. "You got any liquor in the house?"

Dice pointed toward her bar with the silver crescent moons on it. "A whole quart."

After the beheading ceremony, both sides got down to serious negotiations and the issue soon became clear. The next intergalactic bat to visit this planet would land in Rhodesia, and it would be the duty of whichever sect then controlling this territory to feed him. Human flesh is required of course but Verwoerd's CFAP maintained it should be female while Count Guano and his followers insisted the male of the species was far superior.

Euridice Williams. Five feet, one inch. 135 pounds. Medium brown coloring. Fair breasts, tough defiant ass, muscular arms and thighs, putting on weight around the middle, slender ankles. Born Oct. 28, 1932. Raised by her great aunt and uncle [until he left with another woman for Chicago]. Educated in all negro public and high schools, first sex at 13, graduated second in her class. Gave birth to a baby girl, father already married. One arrest, prostitution, no conviction.

At dawn Guano, Verwoerd and the other high priests retired to their coffins with nothing resolved. Dr. Frankenstein, who only becomes a vampire after an injection of a certain rare drug, paced the giant chamber angrily.

Sex of the IGB's food supply was, in reality, unimportant so long as it was white like the bird's sacred dropping (non-whites are used for sacrifices only when the bat itself is not present. This procedure gives the white masses a sense of security between IGB visits).

I took a nap around noon and dreamed I was in bed with one of the white kitchen maids at Henley. In that sub-cellar next to the furnace room.

Between jobs the money gets a little tight, both Dice and I are a little edgy. But I tell her we're going to make out and we always do.

"You got enough money in your purse for a bottle?"

She lights her cigarette. "Shit, you'll soon be living off me."

"Think I'd make a good pimp?"

Dice gives me the you-don't-exist sign, hand up todown, like drawing a window shade.

"I got some money coming to me at the end of the week."

"You'd better have." She laughs, deep and earthy. "Or I'll get myself another man."

"Girl, you never had it so good."

"Shit, you can take your white ass somewhere else anytime you want." She opens her purse and comes up with a twenty. "That has to pay for groceries until your next cheque comes in."

"Okay, a quart of Johnny Walker red and 10 dollars worth of groceries."

Dice hands me the 20. "You're going to be a stone alcoholic."

I take a mock swipe at her bottom. "Look who's talking."

At 5.00 Dr. Frankenstein summoned me to his office. He had been drinking heavily all day and talked more than usual.

Through his own scientific accomplishments the old man had worked his way up into this planet's hierarchy, at least the lower echelons of it. But his position was still inferior to incompetents like Verwoerd and Guano.

Frankenstein poured me a drink, lowered his voice. An intergalactic bat, the Universe's only inorganic life form, had absolutely no conscious will of its own. An IGB followed blindly the laws of cause and effect. But all of this could be changed if hung around the neck of each human eaten by the bird are two secret talismans known only to Dr. Frankenstein. The first would place him under Frankenstein's control, the second would give this IGB supernatural strength to carry himself and up to three humans on its back beyond the Universe where, freed from the cycle of cause andeffect, they would live continuously forever.

That night's meeting began with the strangulation of three oriental women, performed by Frankenstein's sister, and ended again in deadlock.

On the late late show.
Dr. Frankenstein and his creature.
Tangle.
With the vampire priests.
Euridice and I kill.
The last of the scotch.
After making love.
On the screen.
Frankenstein's creature.
Crashes his flying saucer.
And it's time to sleep..

The bargaining, and human sacrifices dragged on for weeks without any sign of progress. Meanwhile the populations of Rhodesia became increasingly restless. It was decided to calm the Rhodesians down by showing them that they were better off than the rest of the world. To accomplish this the KIA, through its connections in Washington and Peking, escalated the Vietnam war. The Kalahari Intelligence Agency also organized race riots in several large American cities including Michigantown. These activities were co-ordinated under the code name Project S.

With advance knowledge of the riots, I moved Dice out to a summer place in the country for a month.

The bloodshed and destruction also made it easier to enforce segregation—which would assure an adequate supply of all white food stuffs for the intergalactic bat.

But none of this was getting Dr. Frankenstein any nearer to his goal. He wanted to personally supervise the feeding of the IGB so that he, his sister and one other person of Frankenstein's choosing (he hinted it might be me) could, garbed in life support suits, take that ride beyond the Universe.

A breeze had sprung up.

Dice went to the window and let it blow over her bared shoulders. Think about the city, harlem, hustling on the street, at Jack's, hot everywhere, and it never cools off. "Can't nobody see me?"

"Not way out here."

She took off her blouse.

Already the IGB is close enough to our solar system that we can receive its radio signals on channel 5. As a result of my superior technological skills, we were the first monitoring station on Earth to pick up those radio pulses produced when the intergalactic bat's heart beats once every 1337 seconds.

Everytime that Frankenstein heard it, he became more desperate to secure his position on the Rhodesian feeding grounds.

I poured myself a little more scotch. "You know, someday we're going to be rich and famous."

Dice returned from the bedroom with another pack of cigarettes. "When?"

I laughed. "Maybe two or three years from now."

"Shit, more like twenty, and I'll be dead by then."

Every night while Verwoerd and Guano debated the merits of each sex, Dr. Frankenstein contemplated "the awful vastness and inconceivable beauty of the glittering worlds which stud, like jewels, the dark canopy of our Midnight sky. And beyond these myriad galaxies of starry systems, continuous life and boundless freedom." All he needed was that interfalactic bat.

Finally Frankenstein devised a desparate plan. He went to Guano and they came to a secret agreement. If Frankenstein could persuade the S. African forces to renounce their claims to Rhodesia, Guano would put the doctor in charge of feeding the IGB. Then Frankenstein went to Verwoerd's protege, Worster, (who like Frankenstein has come up through the ranks) and they, too, made a clandestine pact. If the Doctor removed Verwoerd from the scene, Worster, who'd then automatically become CFAP's high priest, would withdraw from the Rhodesian controversy in favor of Count Guano.

Whereupon, at high noon, Dr. Frankenstein with my assistance carried Verwoerd's coffin to the courtyard, opened it and exposed the sleeping vampire. In an instant his carcass became common bird shit.

(3) *In March 68, although still attached to the Kalahari project,*

57

they gave me a month's vacation. I rented that place in the country again [under an assumed name of course] and the first nice day, April 4, we drove out there. Dice bought all the groceries we needed in advance—chops, cold cuts, a couple of pizzas—everything we needed but the scotch, which I got at the liquor store on Illinois avenue on our way out to the country.

She waited in the car while I went in and got it. A bunch of steel workers just off shift and I had to stand in line. The place was still decorated for St. Patrick's day.

They staged the official assassination of Herr Verwoerd with one of Dr. Frankenstein's androids.

I put the liquor in my trunk and we started out for the country. Dice also had a flask in her purse.

"I hope that damned space heater's working okay. We're really gonna need the fuckin thing tonight."

I took the ramp at 25 then picked up speed as I worked my way into the mainstream of Expressway traffic. "I checked both it and the kitchen stove when I opened the place up."

Dice glanced back to make sure there wasn't a cop on our tail, then opened her purse and took a pull from that flask. "You can't have none while you're driving."

I nodded.

As soon as Frankenstein was placed in charge of the IGB's feeding, he immediately began putting together those secret talismans in his castle laboratory.

Dice turned on the car radio which was already tuned to that Negro FM station. "We've only got one life, let's live it together" by Ruby Winters and Johnny Thunder.

"You want to listed to that shit?"

I shrugged and she located one of the white stations playing jazz.

"That stuff gets on my nerves after while." Dice took one more long pull from the flask, banged the cork in tight and put it back into her purse.

Frankenstein's first talisman was a miniature coffin filled with carefully selected, then dried, brain cells. The exact arrangement of these cells remains his secret. Although the doctor often confides in me, he keeps this bit of information to himself.

Our summer place is an old farm house, a couple of miles off the Expressway, at the end of a dirt lane. At this time of year you've got to drive it carefully because the damn thing is pretty wet and full of holes. In April, if it rains hard you can't get in or out until it dries a little.

I furnished the place mostly with used stuff from a combination cut-rate furniture and pawn shop on Illinois Avenue [anything that'll come through their front door they'll give you a few bucks for.] When Michigantown has another riot this tummer, that'll be the first place to burn.

The brown lane with green on each side is like another recurring dream I used to have before I met Dice, then later while I was away from her in the Kalahari.

When we left Michigantown the sun was shining brightly with some wind gusts and temperatures in the 60s. Now it had begun to cloud up pretty good.

"Shit, you'd better drive this son of a bitch before that rain starts."

"We'll make it." I crawled along at 10 miles an hour.

The doctor's second talisman is a shrunken human heart. This shrinking process alters the chemistry of the tissues which then act as a stimulant in the IGB's bloodstream. Frankenstein allows no one, not even the hag, to observe his shrinking process.

Only two rooms in the house were furnished—a combination living/sleeping room with that space heater at one end, and the kitchen. A larger room in the center of the house had been cleared out so I could paint it; we never used the upstairs anyway.

By the time we got inside there were a few lightning flashes on the horizon. Dice turned on the lights and pulled the shades.

I set a box of groceries down in front of the fridge. "Girl, you're not really scared of lightning, are you?"

"You know it." She wore a light green spring suit. "Are you hungry yet?"

"Uh hun."

"Okay, you fix us a couple of drinks and I'll put on some chops." She located a frying pan beneath the sink.

I went outside again and got the liquor from my trunk. When I came back inside, Dice had put on the TV which you could watch from the kitchen. I checked and found ice in the fridge. "What about the rest of these groceries?"

"I'll put them away while the chops are frying." The TV announcer started on exhibition baseball scores. "Hey, put it on the movies."

I presented her with a drink, took mine into the other room, switched to channel 5 and "Frankenstein—1970."

In January 1967 the doctor spelled it out. He wanted me to accompany him and his sister on that ride beyond the Universe.

Meanwhile the masses had not yet been told that the Rhodesian dispute was settled. Frankenstein decided to withold this, and continue Kalahari's Project S in the interests of maintaining a pure food supply for the approaching IGB.

"Set up a couple of those TV tables." She had fixed some salad to go with those chops. "What kind of dressing do you want, French or blue cheese?"

"Blue cheese." I set up the tables. "Bring the bottle with you."

"Damn, you're going to be shot down by 10.00 o'clock. Get it yourself; I can't carry everything at once."

I did and refilled both our glasses. "Want some more ice for yours?" Dice nodded.

By June 1967 Count Guano became suspicious of that secret work which was going on in Frankenstein's lab. Therefore as a safety precaution, the doctor, again with my assistance, exposed Count Guano to the noonday sun and another vampire was reduced to fertilizer.

The liquor had just begun to work and those chops tasted pretty good too.

At 7.30 they interrupted the movie to say that Martin Luther King had been shot.

Another phase in Kalahari's Project S.

"Oh, my God." Dice reached across and pushed the sound up.

Frankenstein offered to make me head of Guano's LRSP until the intergalactic bat arrived.

At 8.00 they announced that Martin Luther King was dead.

Dice shook her head. "There's gonna be shit now." She killed a drink and refilled it.

On the TV they began the life of Dr. Norman Vincent Peel, "One Man's Way, CBS' Thursday night movie.

"You want to watch this?" I emptied my glass.

She shrugged. "There ain't nothing else on."

I contemplated escaping the Universe, spending eternity with Frankenstein and his sister.

"I could get some news on the radio."

Dice lit a cigarette. "Anything important will come over the TV."

They interrupted a deodorant commercial to announce that rioting had broken out in Washington.

Another couple of shots into her glass.

"Take it easy, honey."

"Shit, why?" She laughed. "I'm gonna get shot down and cut your white throat."

I took a mock swipe at her thigh. "I'm bigger than you are."

"Fuck you." She added some more to my glass too.

On the screen my trained eye could make out the IGB's heart beat once every 1337 seconds.

Around 10:00 Dice got up and cleared away our dishes.

"Why don't you wash them in the morning?"

"You don't expect me to do it tonight, do you?" She was sipping her scotch by now. "Hey, turn the heat up."

"Okay."

"Damn, I'm gonna get into something comfortable." She opened her suitcase and got out a sheer white neglige. "Look the other way."

"What the hell for?"

Dice turned out one of the lamps then stirpped down to the waist. Her maroon tipped breasts hung loose.

I always figured that eternity with Dr. Frankenstein would be a little like those long hot days on the Kalahari.

Except that it would always be dark.

Beyond the Universe.

In that sub-cellar next to the furnace room.

And I wake up choking.

The neglige hung down to just above her knees. Working beneath it, she peeled everything else off. In the dim light, I could only vaguely make out the shape of her body and that mass of primordial forest which covered her belly.

Dice folded her clothing atop the suitcase then came back and sat down in front of the TV again. "I suppose you want to take care of some business tonight."

"When you feel like it."

If I turned down his offer, Frankenstein would immediately consider me a security risk.

At 11:00 they began a news special on the assassination. Dice got another pack of cigarettes from her suitcase. "You want to watch this, don't you?"

"Yes, honey."

Dice retrieved her drink, went over to the bed, and watched from there. By now we were both pretty high.

"Aren't you cold wearing just that nightgown?"

"Put the heat up a little."

61

Outside it had begun to rain again.

Each second brings Frankenstein's intergalactic bat nearer its human food supply. Unless I escape from the KIA, which is unlikely, I'll either take that ride with the doctor or I will be fed to his bird. He has already made two talismans to hang around my neck just in case I should disappoint him.

Except when I am here with Dice, I am always on the run, I have always been running, to prove I belong loose on this Earth, that I'm a man, that I can do anything any other man can do, running to stay out of Dr. Frankenstein's Henley Institute.

The special was almost over. A panel was discussing what the death of Martin Luther King would do to the civil rights movement.

Euridice lay on her stomach, propped up on one elbow.

I went across to the bed and sat on the edge beside her.

It was over and they began on the baseball scores again. I started to undress.

If I become bored beyond the Universe, Frankenstein's sister has volunteered her services.

I pulled up the nightgown and ran my hands over the roughened skin of Euridice's bare buttocks. In a moment she rolled over and we lay together.

I banged her belly and thighs like that IGB would arrive on planet Earth tomorrow. Until Frankenstein's devouring bird swoops, I'm going to be a man no matter how many they kill on the Kalahari.

Stars, planets, galaxies, the Universe expanding to its outer limits. Then the whole astral system begins to collapse upon itself. Each billion years the night sky becomes a little brighter until the end when everything is fire.

I screwed Dice even harder and we both came.

According to the laws of cause and effect, the cycle will repeat exactly as it was before, the Universe expands towards its outer limits, we each live again, according to the laws of cause and effect, exactly as it was before—once every 82 billion years.

And we both came.

The Pynchon Theory As It Applies To The Earth Paradox

It has been alleged by many noted literary historians that **Kurt Vonnegut Jr.** also wrote under several pseudonyms. These include "the man from UNCLE", William Burroughs, Ray Bradbury, Michael Moorcock (notorious science fiction pornographer and founder of *New Worlds*), Lee Wallek (a critic whose works appear in the literary annual *December*) and Thomas Pynchon. But, for the purposes of this preliminary study, it is unnecessary to establish the validity of these claims as we are interested only in those works which bear the Pynchon imprint.

(It should be noted however that the Bradbury hymn to Apollo 8, "Christus Apollo", has become the official anthem of Ironside's Church of the True America. "In this time of Christmas/This holy time of Christmas/Like him, you are God's son!" Therefore the Vonnegut/Pynchon/Bradbury relationship should be further explored at some later date. An equally important future exploration, but at the opposite end of the Vonnegut spectrum, would be espousal in 1972 under the Moorcock imprint of the cyclic universe thesis originally put forth in 1968 by Orpheus in his subversive "Notes From The Kalahari".

Although he does not use the term, all the works of "Thomas Pynchon" deal with anti-matter, more specifically the effects of alternately possible realities on the "real" world. "silent doppleganger Katje (who was *her* opposite number in Sudwest? what black girl he never saw, hidden always in the blinding sun..."—*Gravity's Rainbow*. Or Margherita Erdmann, alternately the victim in Hitler's favorite whipping film and child murdering hag. In *The Crying of Lot 49*, Pynchon deals with a subculture dedicated to the maintenance of its own alternate postal system and which may or may not be responsible for altering the course of history. This is comparable to the DX subculture in that both are interested in exotic alternate forms of communications as an escapist vehicle. And his first novel, *V*, also centers around a message, paradoxical software, anti-matter.

65

("A 20th century DXer would have gone to almost any length to obtain a QSL confirming his reception of Radio Zambia yet described the music heard as "mostly sedate but sometimes wild caterwauling". As noted in *December*, vol. 15, "There are some DX freaks who would be perfectly happy to log exotic stations whose transmissions had no more content than an OTH radar 'blip' '")

"Travelling through strange parts in these days of gas uncertainty can be tricky business. One way to avoid problems is to stay abreast as you travel. How do you do this? We suggest your car's radio. The stations in our list can be heard over much of their home states. Not only do they broadcast information about gas lines and laws but they are also sources of other valuable knowledge. Weather forecasts, traffic conditions, attractions to see, places to eat and stay as well as sporting and recreational events"—

Mechanix Illustrated, July 1974

(By 1975 the Pentagon and other associated agencies had developed a workable system of super powered transmitters which would block out unwanted shortwave anti-matter by altering the ionosphere. Unfortunately the ionosphere interacted with the troposphere, altered weather patterns and brought on an ice age.) (At the end of the Gutenberg Galaxy/Super Critic and Wonder Woman

Are in the Batmobile
On the run
From something   —*SPR* #15)

One of the stations on MI's list, WFIG (Sumter, S.C.) is a former employer of R.Swan's Horton H. Heath. This was probably a deliberate attempt by Orpheus to manipulate reality through print anti-matter. A conspiracy to create a new set of inter-connections, one more alternate scenario. This issue appeared on newsstands at the height of the Watergate controversy, just as Nixon was preparing what turned out to be his final defense perimeter.

(And we are the sideshow freaks
Purusha's mistakes
Who dream
of giants)   —*December*, vol. 15)

Euridice in her red cadilac.

Just as Pynchon's blond double agent, Katje, and the unseen black girl represent alternates—both in themselves and to reality, a similar relationship exists between Titania and Purusha, both as creatures of anti-matter universes, and Euridice aka Wonder Woman.

WONDER WOMAN STRIPS EVERYTHING OFF
but a sleeveless
jet black blouse...............which contrasted
in African shades   with
her mahogany skin

Dice is watching television in my room at the Atlantis while I search through a final half dozen of *Mechanix Illustrated* from the university. We have just sent down for another bottle.

A little comfort along the way.

"In 1961 the CIA's portable was involved in the Bay of Pigs debacle. Several books have been written on this intriguing piece of contemporary history but for the purpose of this article it is only important to note that shortly thereafter the U.S. military decided to set up its own portable broadcast strike force....The Pentagon system, known as the 'Flying Radio City' although not intended for operation while in flight, was built by Gates....In the fall of 1965 Rhodesia made its unilateral declaration of independence and the BBC, or more precisely the British Diplomatic Wireless Service hastily set up a medium and short wave relay station at Francistown, Bechuanaland (now Botswana). According to an expert eye witness account the initial unit was a '50 KW Gates transmitter...on the air within 24 hours' "—*Electronics Today International*, March 1975

In *Gravity's Rainbow* British propaganda ("The White Visitation") forge a film about African rocketmen in Europe which turns out to be true. Related to this is a vile dream sequence in which Malcolm X (unnamed) appears as a menacing shoeshine boy. Excluding the racist content intended by their fictional creators, both represent examples of anti-matter becoming reality, at least within the perimeters of the overall work.

(About those experiments which brought on the ice age—"Although the effects on the economy of long distance communications is now only at best a guess, it seems likely that future radio communications can be vastly improved and that the upper atmosphere will be better understood as a result of this current research project"—

—*Commerce Today*, Oct. 18, 1971)

"If in the structure of his books Pynchon duplicates the intricate networking of contemporary technology, political, and cultural systems, then in the style and rapid transition he tries to

67

match the dizzying tempos, the accelerated shifts from one mode of experience to another, which characterize contemporary media and movement. . . . This is a cumulative process with no predictable direction, so that any summary is pretty much a product of whatever creative paranoia the book induces in a reader"

—Richard Poirier, *Saturday Review*, March 1973

(While print anti-mater, SR would be categorized as quasi-literary rather than pulp as *Mechanix Illustrated, Electronics Today International*, etc. Its circulation and therefore power was somewhat less than *MI's*)

"Although Plastic Man and Sundial are directly mentioned, Superman, Batman and Captain Marvel, the superheroes of World War II comics, determine the tone and conduct of many of the characters"   —*SR*

(Major league woman, minor league man

Minor league man

Better make it while you can)

But in this area Orpheus carried Pynchon's work one step further and created from the comic book super hero a new, fictional mass media on an international scale. "Someday comic strips such as Superman, Green Lantern and 'Capt. Glotz' may be distributed worldwide via shortwave. . . . (Orpheus) was referring to Short Wave Facsimile broadcasting (SWF) used to distribute weather charts and other graphic material to ships at sea"—*Buffalo Courier Express*

Just as the hero of *Gravity's Rainbow* dons a Super Pig costume, Captain Glotz is a disguise worn by Horton H. Heath or one of his network of interchangeable agents (Hunt, Houston etc.). "This possible source of FAX/development comes down to a question of contingency planning: will the Pentagon decide that a viable SW FAX media, given the deficiencies of ionospheric propagation, would be a useful alternative to satellites broadcast capabilities? If they decide it wouldn't, then it is up to the individual experimenter to at least begin the job" —*Electronics Today International*

("Aren't you nearly finished with that shit?" Dice finishes another pack of cigarettes from her purse.)

Captain Glotz is also a right wing DX sub-culture parody of an underground parody. "Captain Guts was originally Fillmore Grinchbottom, average mild-mannered statistician, who turns into tough-mean-clean-dirty-commie-pink-o-dope-fiend-hater, a savior of America with guts instead of 'S' on his chest upon drinking a certain Frab....later changed to All American beer. 'Now! At last!! There's someone with *Guts* enough to stand up for *America*'. "—*SPR* #17. In one respect, Captain Glotz is the real Horton H. Heath/Robert Houston/E. Howard Hunt.

"If a global audience *is* the goal, this means (as weird as it may seem) forms which would be suitable for short wave facsimile broadcasting. And it is weird because at present all SW FAXcasts are controlled entirely by the military with, until recently, no equipment available to the general public for their reception (or transmission)"—

—Orpheus (aka Super Critic) in *SPR* #17

In the obscure electronics publication *VHF-UHF DIGEST* A Kansas DXer repeatedly speculated on a link between rare reception and killer tornados.

"This kind of speculative writing abounds in the book, brilliantly bringing together technological and much earlier analytical methods that combine to the eventual distortion of lives"—*SR*. The newsstand has become an interface between reality and anti-matter, part of a subversive print network stretching into the deepest black holes. Orpheus plans to replace the newsstand with shortwave facsimile receivers.

(Nightmares of black women seized by Canadian border guards. Dreams of science fiction sets hidden behind the magazine racks.)

Gravity's Rainbow is of course constructed around Earth's first space vehicle—what SR describes as "the ultimate whip....sex, love, life, death have all been fused into the Rocket's assembly and into its final trajectory." The amazing thing about *Gravity's Rainbow* is that it was written before Watergate.

("Do you want to take care of business tonight or don't you." Euridice stands naked by the bed. I take a mock swipe at her buttocks with the last MI.)

Even beyond the perimeter of the book itself, *Gravity's Rainbow*'s anti-matter became reality. "Nixonian America's conquest of the Moon represents an archetypal symbol of power"— *December*, vol. 13. Publication was after the burglary but the text was certainly completed before that event (just as Orpheus' infamous "The Nixon Capers" was written before the president was forced from office.)

Orbit   Orpheus final journey from the Kalahari home to Euridice took him across Zambia's copper belt, Mozambique's tropical rain forest, the Indian ocean port of Perth

69

(here in 1975 the Pentagon was implicated in some further short-wave intrigue), Rushcutters Bay near Sydney where *Electronics Today International* was published and then, carrying the subversive software seeds emanating from ETI with him, across the pacific to America's west coast. The long path, a brilliant anti-matter maneuver.

("America fill the universe with fruit!")

("This is a cumulative process with no predictable direction, so that any summary is pretty much the product of whatever creative paranoia the book induces.")

Pynchon's two major works, *Gravity's Rainbow* and *"V"*, center primarily around Germanic technological fantasy, first in Southwest Africa, then Europe. But from the Bay of Pigs on, the action shifted to America.

(The bed springs have taken to screeching)

A rocket

Inner Earth

The only pussy worth a damn

"Take it easy, honey"

I reach beneath her and grab a handful of ass. We both come.

(*END*)

The Nixon Capers

Ironside as Super Critic
"Sherlock Holmes is so much the type of the intuitive genius it is unnecessary to dwell at length on the characteristics of the mind. It is a mind for which situations are total and inclusive unities. Every facet, every item of a situation, for Holmes, has total relevance"—Marshall McLuhan, *Explorations No. 8*

Ironside as PR man
"Although Epstein's radical titles sold comparatively well, continuing to justify his earlier Random House editorial policies, it occured to him that Bennett Cerf, never quite a fire-eating radical himself, and/or his colleagues might repudiate this policy. They had previously resisted Epstein's ambition to publish Barbara Garson's *Macbird* (1965), a heavy handed script that probably attracted the mob (and antagonized Cerf) because it vulgarized their own increasing antipathy toward President Johnson...MacDonald produced an extravagantly laudatory notice in *The New York Review [of Books]* "—Richard Kostelanetz, *December*, vol. 15

The latter quotation, an excerpt from "The End of Intelligent Writing" was published in August 1973. Four months later Epstein's NYRB returned to the JFK assassination conspiracy motif with Gore Vidal's "The Art and Arts of E. Howard Hunt".

The private eye as culture hero
"one of Washington's more controversial propaganda outlets (Radio Americas), supposedly operated by the Central Intelligence Agency, was either instead operated by the Pentagon, or served primarily as cover for a top secret military installation."

"In 1963 Lee Harvey Oswald was connected with an organization which broadcast over Radio Americas."

"during the 1962 Cuban missile crisis...the Radio Americas identity was...emanating from locations within the United States itself"—

"Through The Looking Glass 1973", *December*, vol. 15

About a month after Super Critic made the above, almost, inadvertant, entry into the mythological world of assassination

73

plots, E. Howard Hunt's "Give Us This Day", a new right wing account of the Bay of Pigs (in which Radio Americas, aka Radio Swan, played a key role) corroborated two of our conclusions: it was primarily a Pentagon rather than a CIA operation, and even at that time the station had multi-site capabilities, i.e. it was designed to transmit from locations other than the publicized one on Swan Island. Then followed the Vidal effort which transforms Hunt from hack propagandist into a figure of almost archetypal evil on the landscape of American mythology.

[Ironside has decided he wants a piece of the action
Walk the street
Make it shake]

And although challenged for a time by the absurd secret agent (*Mission Impossible* prepared America for Watergate), American mythology is primarily the hunting ground of the private eye—as currently represented on Television by Ironside (disguised as a cop and as close as this continent will come to Victorian England's Sherlock Holmes), Madigan and Mannix. A culture can only be viewed objectively from without. These series, by their very nature, involve outsiders in varying degrees. For example, although the initial episode of Madigan followed a basically contrived, and at times banal, story line, the Harlem setting was both erotic (as compared to the traditionally dead-assed white society) and realistic.

[Mannix, on the other hand, is a cop out. He should be screwing his black secretary—private eyes always screw their secretaries]

"Peter wondered if he was to have Tajli as an audience for the remainder of his breakfast, then...her head turned, and he noticed how caucasian her profile and features were...The American revolution is the only one that has proved itself over nearly two centuries"—E. Howard Hunt, "The Towers of Silence"

[For nearly two centuries America has quite literally kept her soul imprisoned in niggertown—collections of shanties and tenements within do-it-yourself white ghettos like Biloxi, Moline and Buffalo—Hunt's hometown]

The evidence which has been made public indicates that Oswald's infiltration of the Cuban Revolutionary Council was brief and, according to them, very superficial. The CRC did produce programs for both R. Swan & Americas, and was for a time under

Hunt's direction. CRC claims Oswald was detected as a plant immediately but if he was as psychotic as the evidence makes it appear then he could have deluded himself into thinking he was still working for the CRC after having been repeatedly rejected by the Marxists.

[*Ironside is an outsider whether he likes it or not*]

Vidal, however, is not content with psychology. Typical of the points raised in NYRB are the following: "Mrs. Odio was an anti-Castro, pro-Manolo Ray Cuban exile who two months before the assassination of President Kennedy was visited in her Dallas apartment by three men. Two were Latins. . . The third, she maintained, was Oswald. . . The Warren Commission and the FBI never satisfactorily identified Mrs. Odio's visitors. Just before the report was finished the FBI reported to the Warren Commission that one Loran Eugene Hall, 'a participant in numerous anti-Castro activities' had recalled visiting her with two other men, one of them, William Seymour, resembling Oswald. But after the report appeared. . . Hall had retracted his story. . . Hall had already been brought to the Commission's attention in June, 1964, under the names of 'Lorenzo Hall, alias Lorenzo Pascillio'. The FBI heard in Los Angeles that Hall and a man called Jerry Patrick Hemming had pawned a 30.06 rifle, which Hall redeemed shortly before the assassination with a check drawn on the account of the 'Committee To Free Cuba'."

[*"Again and again he recurred to the fact that if he could be assured that society was freed from Professor Moriarty he would cheerfully bring his own career to a conclusion"—*

Memoirs of Sherlock Holmes]

[*But which is Moriarty and which is Holmes?*]

"Lee Harvey Oswald was a partisan of Fidel Castro, and an admitted Marxist who made desperate efforts to join the Red revolution in Havana. In the end he was an activist for the Fair Play for Cuba Committee. But for Castro and the Bay of Pigs disaster there would have been no such 'committee'. And perhaps no assassin named Lee Harvey Oswald"—E. Howard Hunt, "Give Us This Day".

[*Why did former CIA agent James McCord, a contributor to the Committee to Investigate Assassinations, blow the Watergate burglary?*]

"I suspect that whoever planned the murder must have been astonished at the reaction of the American establishment. The most vengeful of all the Kennedys made no move to discover who really killed his brother. In this, Bobby was a true American: close ranks, pretend there was no conspiracy, do not rock the boat"—Gore Vidal, NYRB.

[*Orpheus was the original private eye. He went into the under-world in search of Euridice. But he didn't know when to quit digging.*]

The problem is that Vidal, like the Kennedys, is something of a cultural insider. To borrow Kostelanetz' terminology, he is one of the outer leaves of the New York Literary Mob Union, i.e. he does not have the vantage point of the committed outsider nor does he have the insight which (sometimes) results from proximity to real power (McCord?). The fact is that the CIA in the 60s was run by men close to the center of the liberal elements in American culture and, in this respect, John F. Kennedy was one of their own and Hunt the outsider (although certainly not outside the fabric of traditional American culture). If there was an assassination conspiracy, it will be the Central Intelligence Agency, or what was the CIA prior to Nixon's election in 1968, which will revenge it. Not an expose, but revenge.

[*How does one avenge a myth?*]

[*A counter-myth?*]

"What had come to light during a series of revelations in 1967-68 was that (a) the influential European Congress of Cultural Freedom was CIA-subsidized, and (b) the whole cold ⹁war ideology...had all come from one central source"—Maxwell Geismar, *December*, vol. 11

"Have the much publicized efforts of the Central Intelligence Agency in the area of global thought control become merely a front for the military's much more advanced experiments on the same battleground?"—super Critic in *December*, vol. 15

["*Euridice Williams, five foot, one inch, 135 pounds, medium brown coloring, fair breasts, maroon tipped, tough defiant ass, muscular arms and thighs...born Oct. 28, 1932*"—*December, Vol 13*]

"A myth currently popular in academia contends that man is helpless to resist not only biological but technological evolution as well; communications types, or stages of media supposedly follow one another according to some predetermined or divine pattern"—

—Notes From Super Critic, SPR No. 15

If in fact the whole Watergate affair is in reality a vendetta launched by the liberal establishment which formerly used the Central Intelligence Agency as its international power base, against a rightist, Pentagon-oriented president then it is significant that the Pentagon still seems to be conducting business as usual. Within hours of the death of Salvadore Allende, the Chilean junta put on the air new high powered short wave transmitters. The speed with which they were put on the air suggests that they were very advanced portable units—hardware which the junta could only have obtained directly from the Pentagon or through some NATO inter-connection. Of course toppling a Marxist regime, even a relatively democratic form of Marxism, would be one way of shoring up support for the Nixon administration amongst conservative Congressmen. If so, what next—another invasion of Cuba and a second missile crisis? A re-writing of the mythology of the 60s?

[*Prowl the street*
A drink at the Thessaloniki
Pick up Euridice
Orpheus [aka Ironside] in Harlem
Before they got the first Kennedy
Myth]

  According to his own "Give Us This Day", at the beginning of what became the Bay of Pigs project Hunt recommended "Assassinate Castro *before* or coincident with the invasion" and "Destroy the Cuban radio and television transmitters before or coincident with the invasion". In short the same pattern of assassination and media seizure as apparently seen in Chile.
[*NIGHTMARE*

Euridice dreams
Ironside can walk
In tie and shirt
He gets up
And knocks her down]

But Hunt was in the pen when they took care of Allende. A perfect alibi. So what are we dealing with: some of Hunt's fellow conspirators, technological evolution working out its own myth, or both?
  [*In one version of the Hindu creation myth the deity Purusha, like a giant spider, secretes an interminable thread, weaves a web with it and then lives in this web"—December, vol. 15*]
  What ever the answer, it's clear that Kostelanetz—probably

77

the number one hustler on the small press scene today—missed a bet when he put down the assassination conspiracy bit so lightly.

The private eye as hustler? In one Ironside episode, he assumes his true identity—a drunken derelict on the street then to raise drinking money, sells his life story to a tabloid just slightly above the level of Candid Press.

[*"For two and a half years yours truly ghosted Walt's weekly whiz-offs for him* [*the poor, Beam-soaked old bastard*] *and reviewed dirty books for CP . . . now, with* Candid Press *defunct* [*dead—along with Walt Whiz*], *I am out of a paying job"—Editorial in December, Vol. 15*]

The mainstream of pornography has to do with power—quite literally naked power: on the street, within Kostelanetz' mythical NY Literary Mob, or on an international scale as in the violent deaths of Kennedy and Allende.

[*"their father makes most of his living today by writing pornography* [*which must also say something about our country and its values . . ."*]—

—*Preface to "The Bonnyclobber", December Press*]

At the time of Radio Swan and the Bay of Pigs there is no doubt, based on "Give Us This Day" and the evidence we collected for *December*, that the CIA was used as cover for the Pentagon and a military operation. Slightly over a decade later, according to both John Dean and an official report of the House Armed Services Committee (or more precisely a sub-committee thereof) the CIA was again used as cover, much less successfully, for a series of illegal domestic intelligence projects which ultimately led to impeachment proceedings agains the President of the United States.

[*Kill the mother fucker*]

Significantly, not only was E. Howard Hunt involved in both operations but on page 40 of "Give Us This Day" Hunt quotes a 1960 conversation with USMC Brigadier General Robert Cushman (later Deputy Director of, i.e. the Pentagon's ambassador to, the CIA at the time of the Ellsberg break-in) in which Cushman states that then Vice President Nixon was the Bay of Pigs project's "action officer within the White House".

With the bungling Agnew conveniently removed from the scene and replaced by solid citizen Ford, Nixon may have become more of a liability than an asset to the Pentagon—better a dead martyr than a live crook. In other words, Nixon might have both sides gunning for him.

None of the assassination conspiracy theories take into account the central mysteries of the 20th century—to what extent does electronic technology with all its hidden interconnections and interchangeable identities determine behavior of outsiders such as Lee Harvey Oswald and E. Howard Hunt? Or, conversely, to what extent do similar minds determine the configurations of that technology in the first place? Or, to invoke a super counter-myth, is Purusha himself a sadistic maniac—a mythic reincarnation of Victorian England's Jack-the-ripper?

"She was a blob of flesh now, drained of even superficial carnality. Nothing to sell but her body, he reflected with perhaps a few routine perversions for the demanding client. . . *This morning at an early hour the body of Signorina Evalina Vitale was found on her blood soaked bed*" —E. Howard Hunt, "The Venus Probe".

"On the subject of name games, that of the fictitious young lady referred to earlier in those LSD notes bears a close resemblance to one of organized DXing's few female members. Thus, in this instance at least, G-2's activities seem to reflect those of an absurd sub-culture"—*December*, vol 15

"By sub-culture we mean one which is separated from the mainstream of the arts, philosophy, religion or generally accepted rules of social conduct. The schism can occur in all four areas, or in only one"—*December*, vol. 10

[*But all that really counts is fucking and staying alive—as soon as Orpheus forgets that he's dead*]

[*The hell with Purusha*]

The web of inter-connections which begins with Radio Swan seems to stretch on endlessly: in includes broadcasts by the Committee to Free Cuba ("Radio Cuba Libre") alluded to by Vidal and NYRB, a station in the Dominican Republic built by dictator Trujillo (himself subsequently assassinated) which originally operated as the clandestine Radio Liberacion de Venezuela, another anti-Castro clandestine known as Radio Escambre Libre (and using one of Radio Swan's alternate transmitter sites) which became Radio Libertad and was subsequently taken over by (or visa versa) that organization responsible for Radio Free Russia (National Alliance of Russian Solidarists). Probably a sub-culture, separate from all others, could be found built around these identities alone none of which (even though it diminishes a myth currently popular in the small press sub-culture) necessarily have any CIA connections.

[*But which is Holmes and which is Moriarty? Could it be that*

the clandestine broadcast world of E. Howard Hunt is the main-
stream of 20th century technology?]

When Hunt praises the American revolution, he has in mind the white aristocrats who controlled it. And when in his spy novels he wishes to compliment a fellow agent, the term "Knight" is used. In "Give Us This Day" the headquarters chief of propaganda operations is assigned the code name "Knight". In short, Sir. E. Howard Hunt, despite an insatiable need to attack British intelligence and British government policies in his books, prefers the Victorian world (upon whose empire the sun never set) of Sherlock Holmes to the reality of Ironside's America. If he cannot make the President a world emperor, Hunt will have him at least a king. And, surface appearances notwithstanding, the only real sex in his novels is in a form approaching that of Jack the Ripper—a truly representative Victorian psychopath. (and are Hunt and the Ripper as mythologically interchangeable as Holmes and Moriarty?)

[*Black Euridice riding*
On a white winter's knight
Fuck it to me
Slow and easy, mama]

And if the Nixon image is beyond repair then what? If "Tricky Dicky" is proven to be just that—a minor league American con man, talented enough to peep through keyholes and peddly dirty books but not much else—how do Hunt and his fellow Victorians save the American aristocracy?

But maybe Orpheus, aka Super Critic, aka Ironside, has
already dug too deep into Purusha's web.

A View from the 60th Century

"Arise, shine; for thy light has come, and the glory of the Lord is risen upon thee. For behold, the darkness shall cover the earth, and gross darkness the people: but the Lord shall arise upon thee, and his glory shall be seen upon thee"—*Isaiah*, Chapter 60

"God damn it, I'm a man"—Orpheus Thrush

I

I am a character in a piece of 20th century. science fiction. Through the miracle of print I have been transported into the year 6000 and it is from this vantage point that I am able to re-examine my roots. But I warn you, I was always an outcast from the mainstream of sf mythology. I am a white private eye (Orpheus Thrush) with a black mistress (Euridice Williams). We do not make love in some abstract, off stage never never land. We fuck and you will not find us in the pages of *Amazing Stories* or *Frontiers*.

"The would-be sf prophet whose works contain a major archetypal vision is in competition with the already established order, and this has kept him at the fringes of the 'respectable' and highly conservative sub-culture"—*Small Press Review* #6-7

"As far as I am concerned, science fiction which must depend upon sexual explicitness is built upion a pretty poor foundation"—Roger Elwood in the preface to *Frontiers* #1. Thus we have in that same issue Robert Silverberg's intergalactic captain ever so slightly lusting for a blind "ship sister" who obviously needs a good screw: they both settle for psychic contact with the stars (a prospect which was not likely to alarm the existing order on 20th century Earth), and ("Mutation Planet") Barrington J. Bayley's red haired research assistant who "gave a deep sigh that strained her full breasts against her smock" (a line worthy of the equally conservative but less pretentious *Amazing Stories*) after which she is eaten by the notoriously asexual "Dominus" —a good old fashioned space opera monster also worthy of *Amazing Stories*.

[*Euridice's mahogany buttocks are like the two hemispheres of our planet. She looks back over her shoulder at me. "Quit acting like a dog in heat."*]

In the early 1950s Ray Palmer was hastily dispatched as the editor of *Amazing Stories* after he announced that flying saucers were "real". If he'd waited a few years he would have been right. There was the Soviet Sputnik I in 1957 then in 1961, after the Bay of Pigs incident, the conquest of space became really serious business. But Palmer still would have been fired.

(You don't think there's anything sexual about space conquest? Well, as one evangelist—Carl McIntire of the 20th Century Reformation Hour—put it, when he saw the giant Apollo rocket blast off he knew Christ was coming again)

Of course, despite his performance in *Frontiers*, Bayley was capable of major league work. As in *New Worlds Quarterly* #1—"If the symbols were rounded, square, on the Jungian mandala or quaternity patterns, then he was pleased. The image he looked for was the cave, the female, the square table, the square room, the circle. Today there was an altogether unacceptable number of thrusting, probing images, the tower on the plain, the pointed lance, the long journey, the Magician, the supreme effort... Aware of the part played by the sexual polarity in the structure of the social psyche, Kord had long recognized that it was necessary to create a womb-centered, vulva-centered civilisation, instead of a phallus-centred one." Or as evangelist Dan Gilbert put it shortly after the Bay of Pigs—"Faced with indignation over the. . .Cuban fiasco, President Kennedy. . .rushed before Congress to appeal for forty more million dollars to finance a ten year program 'to beat the Russian Communists to the moon'. . .The realm over which man has authority to reign is the earth and nothing but the earth. . .The 'builders of the tower of Babel' wanted to leave earth and 'reach onto heaven' (Genesis II). God confounded their presumptuous experiment and their tower was sent crashing down to earth."

(Nixon broods at San Clemente
He dreams of violence)

That's where I came in—the Bay of Pigs. I was a kind of wireman, something like James McCord who eventually blew the lid off the Watergate caper, but my specialty was short wave—either broadcasting or private transmissions. I'd tune around for something unusual, follow it through until I came up with a story, most of the time some minor league technological scandal, then sell it to the highest bidder (shit, what do you think this is, the wheel chair olympics?), usually a magazine editor. I paid a lot of Euridice's bills that way, but my pet project, the case I really wanted to break, was the Bay of Pigs.

Euridice likes to bug me. "I cut the story on you out of the Courier, and threw it in the garbage."

"Shit."

(In light of Bayley's "The Four-Color Problem" in *NWQ#2*, his appearance in the dismal *Frontiers* becomes almost inexplicable. The Four-Color Problem" challenges (parodies) both William Burroughs (minus the queer stuff) and indirectly, although he is not mentioned, Thomas Pynchon—the two masters of 20th century literature, both of whom wrote science fiction yet were totally unconnected with the sf sub-culture. But this is no parody. I am deadly serious.)

"The secret ambition of a great many shortwave listeners is to single-handedly uncover a piece of international intrigue. The radio waves themselves offer enormous opportunities to do just that. For example, beginning with a single piece of unusual transmission during the Cuban missile crisis, when Radio Americas switched IDs with VOA sites....we determined that it was primarily a military rather than a CIA operation. We further learned that it was capable of transmitting from secret locations other than the publicized Swan Island site. Now these conclusions have been confirmed by none other than E. Howard Hunt of Watergate fame....

(Prior to the fall of 1961, Radio Americas was known as Radio Swan. The name change occured about a year before the missile crisis and around the same time that the Pantagon's Defense Intelligence Agency was created as a completely separate entity from the civilian run Central Intelligence Agency.)

....According to Hunt's book, the original Bay of Pigs blueprint consisted of three parts. First, a Cuban expeditionary force would establish a beach head and 'government-in-arms". Second, Radio Swan transmitting from Swan Island 'and elsewhere' would broadcast appeals for help on behalf of the government-in-arms. Finally, with these widely heard Radio Swan broadcasts as justification, there would be massive Pentagon intervention. Someone, apparently the newly elected President John F. Kennedy, cancelled all but the first part of the plan"—

—Popular Electronics, Oct. 1974

Now go back and read those last three paragraphs over again

carefully (both Radios Swan and Americas transmitted on 6000 kHz.)

(One shortwave broadcast station—which for the purposes of this fiction we shall raname the Voice of Chile—dedicated the entire year of 1974 to aiding the handicapped which for American listeners served as a neat diversion from Watergate and Howard Hunt. Shades of Silverberg in *Frontiers*)

(Possibly Bayley's *Frontiers* piece is a secret parody of the sf sub-culture—including his confusion of the terms race and species? As in "The Four-Color Problem" where Reverend Kludd tells his congregation "It is no sin to kill a nigger, for in God's eyes a nigger is no more'n a dawg.")

22nd day of the 11th month—President John F. Kennedy died from an assassin's bullet

4th day of the 4th month—Martin Luther King Jr. assassinated

6th day of the 6th month—Robert F. Kennedy died from an assassin's bullet

8th day of the 8th month—Richard M. Nixon announced his resignation as President of the United States

What Palmer was looking for at *Amazing Stories* with his flying saucers was something that would open up the mysteries of the Universe while at the same time make him rich and famous. That's what I'm after too.

Throughout the mid 20th century two loosely defined but powerful groups contended for control of the non-Marxist parts of the Earth and, ultimately—at first almost by accident, man's conquest of space. One had as its power base the Central Intelligence Agency and tended toward non-violent forms of subverjsion; clandestine support of liberal-left politicians, trade unions, mildly radical academic journals and indigenous elements of the mass media. A second operated through the U.S. Pentagon and had a propensity for right wing dictatorships, military force and violence. John F. Kennedy and his brother Robert were typical of the first, Nixon of the second.

("The U.S. military at such facilities as the Air Force's Cambridge Research Laboratories have developed various computer techniques for removal of 'picture noise'. One such technique involves enhancing only those patterns which conform to a loosely prescribed geometry, or by distorting contrasts...as noted by the author in vol. 15 of the American cinema and literary annual, *December*, the U.S. military, especially from the Bay of Pigs on, has become ever increasingly involved in international broadcasting to the general public"—

—Electronics Today International, Australian edition, Feb. 1974

Euridice and I fucked the night Nixon was re-elected.

"Nixonian America's conquest of the moon represents an archetypal symbol of power for the remainder of this planet's inhabitants while permitting white Americans (and any other racial or ethnic group which can bring itself to identify with them) to dig, via mass media, the epic adventure of space exploration while ignoring the other, soon to be segregated, corners of this globe"—

—Thrush in *December,* vol. 13 (1971)

"One of my black brothers recently accused me of oppresing him 'for more than 400 years'. The accusation was based on the observable fact that my skin is white. Now, I haven't been around for 400 years, worse luck, but I have been around long enough to research this question further back then 400 years. I have news for my black brother. Whites have been oppressing blacks and blacks oppressing whites a helluva lot longer than 400 years—

—Frank Herbert's introduction to *Frontiers* #1

It was the initial Kennedy assassination which made it impossible for the American far right to embrace, and ultimately—during the Nixon presidency—profit from, space exploration.

II

As I am writing this from the "60th" century, I guess I should tell you something about it. Let me quote from a very early work of science fiction, The Book of Revelations—"and the sound of harpers and minstrels, of flute players and trumpeters, shall be heard in thee no more . . . . . and the light of the lamp shall shine no more, and the voice of the bridegroom and bride shall be heard in thee no more".

Euridice wants to know if she can have her rent money a couple of days early this month.

"Let us again call attention to the words of Jesus which we quoted from Luke 21, 11 'And fearful sights and great signs shall there be from heaven' . . . . . . These signs which Christ said would appear could well include the flying saucers"—

—Gordon Lindsey, Radio & TV evangelist

"We landed on Venus in a desert near the equator, first spraying the area with poison gas which killed every living thing within a radius of 100 miles. This assured there would be no interference while we set up our base and former Voice of America station."

"Once on the air, Commander Straker declared to all Venutians within range that their savior had arrived."

"The Venutians had aircraft, radio, television and a form of planetary government, but they were no match for us militarily. We easily anti-materialized several reconnaisence planes and a squadron of bombers which they sent over our encampment."

"Meanwhile in a series of pinpoint raids, we kidnapped key Venutian military and government personnel, along with their families. Venutians are smaller than we are, between four and five feet, with light green skin. But when cut with a whip or knife, they bleed red blood just like us. Straker referred to this as the Christmas effect."—from "My Visit to Venus".

Prior to the time that it became necessary to remove Nixon from office, Pentagon's final terrestial adventure was the violent overthrow of the Chilean government and establishment of a model dictatorship similar to that responsible for the conquest of Venus.

By this time you probably understand my plan. I have combined an avant guarde political and historical thesis with a powerful archetypal motif—man's conquest of the universe. This operation should be considerably more successful than Palmer's crude flying saucers.

According to a *New York Times* story on the Central Intelligence Agency, the rival "military intelligence establishment" made up "more than four-fifths of the intelligence community" in the U.S. as of 1974. In the sept. 14, 1973 issue of *National Review*, Miles Copeland (who helped organize the CIA in the late 40s) suggested that former Central Intelligence agent, James McCord, led the Watergate burglars into a trap. If so, it is clear that the CIA played a major role in the destruction of Nixon's public image—to the extent that his symbolic assassination became necessary (better a dead martyr than a live crook).

The purpose of Pentagon's Venutian invasion was to set up a series of controlled environments in which various techno-sociological theses could be tested. What sort of communications media would evolve in a city populated entirely by blind persons? Or in one populated by paraplegics? (the works of J.G. Ballard—eg. his "Journey Across A Crater" in *NWQ*#1, figured prominently in these experiments). And there were several environments dedicated to the culture of violence—the Kennedy/

King/Kennedy/Nixon paradox: what do the dates mean—I don't know ("The secret ambition of a great many shortwave listeners is to single-handedly uncover a piece of international ingrigue").

[*"Get your ass over here, woman. I need to forget about this Watergate shit for a few hours."*]

"As they embraced, the curved balcony of the unused terrace enclosed them like an amputated limb. The eyes of the insane watched them in intercourse."—from "Journey Across A Crater"

(I don't know what the dates mean.)

"All (*organized*) international broadcast listening in North America is carried on by DX (distant or rare reception—Thrush) clubs. Up until about 1960 such organizations were controlled entirely by illiterates (in the broadest sense of the term). While this has now changed, the rank and file members of these clubs still consist of very young teenagers, egotistical rednecks with George Wallace mentalities...and neurotics just slightly above the level of George Wallace's would-be assassin" —*December*, vol. 15

By the 60th century Pentagon plans to evacuate Earth, under cover of anti-matter warfare, of their most loyal subjects (the Anglo-Saxons) then destroy it, thus permanently ending all forms of subversion. The Cuban missile crisis was designed to test public reaction to just such a world war.

(Remember we are living in a science fiction universe)

"The time may come in the distant future when God will decide to create life on other planets in the Universe. And we may have a very direct part in it! That's the awesome destiny God holds out for all mankind." —Worldwide Church of God (1973)

An article in the Sept. 30, 1974 *Newsweek* contained the following statement—"The CIA has also made a major effort in recent years to improve the cover used by agents overseas...In 1968, a special CIA-unit was set up to put deep-cover 'assets' in place. Some agents now even pose as missionaries." We submit that if there were agents posing as missionaries even as early as the 20th century, the majority of them were *not* connected with the Central Intelligence Agency.

(Lee Harvey Oswald, before assassinating President Kennedy, was briefly in contact with an organization which produced programs for the Pentagon's Radio Americas.)

"They were suspended in the center of the cavity, He was gripping Polla by her upper arms, and she his. Their bodies, held away from each other while he thrust between her legs, and joined at the genitals, were arched violently and bucking like wild animals, savagely butting, fucking."—Bayley porno from *NWQ#1*

(The 60th Century exists not in time but in print. It is anti-matter.)

Every place you go in this science fiction universe there are super broads like Polla. But the only pussy worth a damn comes from Earth. *"You remember my girl friend Polla Rivers, she just called from Erie to say she'd been saved by Reverend Kludd."*

"From what?"

"Shit, don't talk like that."

"Well, Polla can do what she wants but don't you go religious on me or I'll beat your ass."

The Worldwide Church of God also produced one series of programs for the Pentagon's Radio Swan.

(Nixon broods at San Clemente

He dreams of violence)

The Venutian experiments were crucial in determining what sort of social structure would be most suitable for post-terrestial man. The goal is to eliminate both the generalized concept "human" as well as individual identities and replace with more manageable categories—blind, paraplegic, nigger, subversive—or as Reverend Kludd might put it, "Kill a commie for Christ."

Thrush "who has been confined to a wheel chair almost since birth by Cerebral Palsey, has had approximately 250 articles on electronics published. Most have been about international broadcasting. He has become somewhat of a controversial figure in this field because of his work on the "Bay of Pigs' and related subjects."—

—*Buffalo Courier-Express.*

Euridice likes to bug me. "I cut the story on you out of the Courier, and threw it in the garbage."

"Shit."

(I am not a missionary from the Central Intelligence Agency and, anyway, even they don't know what those dates mean.)

"We're in nut country now"—John F. Kennedy just before they shot him (from his wheelchair Governor Wallace endorsed President Nixon's 1973 inauguration speech).

"got it together in '61, got the sounds right the following year, hit it to the top with *Moonsong* in that golden year of the assassination"—Barry N. Malzberg in *Frontiers #1* (one of the few remotely bright spots in this dismal collection: and even in this one the hero kicks his naked mistress out instead of screwing

90

her—Reverend Kludd saves another soul!)

"Many shortwave listeners don't want their 'hobby' to be this serious, and he has often been criticized by some radio clubs for his stress on the clandestine side of things. 'I don't consider shortwave a hobby' says Thrush 'and neither do the various governments who spend millions of dollars every year on such broadcasts'. He was even expelled from one club for his activities."

"American mythology is primarily the hunting ground of the private eye....A culture can only be viewed objectively from without; these series, by their very nature, involve outsiders in varying degrees" —*Small Press Review* #22

Euridice likes to bug me. "I cut the story on you out of theCourier, and threw it in the garbage."

"Shit."

But of course she's right. The whole thing is science fiction, isn't it. This is a black hole and it's filled with anti-matter. Infinite mass within a finite Universe—the laws of fact are suspended.

III

"My Visit To Venus" has its origins in the early 1940s when *Planet Comics* detailed the adventures of a human underground after Earth had been conquered by an alien species. Thrush appropriated this theme in a short story ("The Invasion!") for the Feb-March 1967 *Radio-TV Experimenter*. But a twist has been added—in the end it turns out that the planet under attack is Venus and "we" are the invaders,

"ELECTRONICS GURU FORESEES SHORTWAVE COMIC STRIPS"—

—*Buffalo Courier Express*

(After he was expelled from the club they began featuring an occasional anti-Thrush comic strip. "They drew me as an evil looking Ironside" says Thrush referring to the famed paraplegic detective, "I was really complimented because the strip was a pretty professional piece of work.")

"I switched on my general coverage converter and began working down through the international shortwave broadcast bands. 16 and 19 metres were absolutely dead but on 15016 kHz some bird with a phony accent and a made-up language was sending messages....I moved on down through 25 and 31 metres which were also blank. Static showed up around 6 MHz but still no stations"—"The Invasion!"

The summer 1942 issue of *Marvel Mystery Comics* contains a story by Mickey Spillane (later to become famous for his own private eye, Mike Hammer) about the first American to conquer the moon. Therefore I am not the first to combine these genres. Spillane's Moon story concludes "It was the ditch he dug, deep enough to be seen from Earth—claiming the Moon for the *United States!*" this same issue of *Marvel Mystery Comics* contains such creations as The Torch and Submariner which further demonstrates that traditionally close relationship between the anti-matter world of "pulp" print (*Amazing Stories, Radio-TV Experimenter, Popular Electronics* etc.) and the science fiction, outsider, superhero.

("Orpheus Thrush, soldier of fortune, expert radio technician and electronic investigator, after being lured to Venus by the Pentagon, and following numerous harrowing adventures, has escaped and returned to Earth. Unfortunately, while trying to land his stolen single passenger flying saucer on Swan Island, he crashed (due to being unfamiliar with the controls) and was unable to resume his previous role as Mike Hammer."—

—from an unpublished Thrush manuscript)

Remember, this is a science fiction universe.

One of the hit records which Malzberg didn't include in his *Frontiers* piece;

Big assed mama, let the good times roll
Let the good times roll.
Need a big assed woman to save my soul

The hell with America's "Moonsong". The only pussy worth a damn comes from Earth.

Once on Venus I was persuaded to attend some sort of special function—I don't remember what the occasion was anymore— staged by the Cerebral Palsey organization. The organization consisted of young CP adults and a few do-gooders, over-dressed society bitches—or church ladies maybe. It turned out they had conned one of the local orchestras (from the blind experiment) into putting on a dance for the CPs. This resembled a cross between Mutation Planet and a Barnum & Bailey freak show. I got the hell out of their as fast as I could.

Euridice williams, boirn Oct. 28, 1932. Raised by her great aunt and uncle—until he left with another woman for Chicago. Educated in all-negro public and high schools. First sex at 13, graduated second in her class. Has hustled on the street, in a bar. One arrest. Her body is a subtle study in earth shades. . . . at 42

Euridice is still a good-looking broad.

In the 60th century Ballard and Bayley are combined—"He waited on the kerb as the attendants helped Polla from her car into the art gallery. When they lifted the chromium trestle on the chasis of the wheelchair the sunlight flashed around her deformed legs".

Nixon broods at San Clemente

He dreams of violence

("Once on the air, Commander Straker declared to all Venutians within range that their savior had arrived")

Thrush "whose articles have appeared regularly in the electronics magazines for the past 15 years, was referring to Short Wave Facsimile broadcasting (SWF), used to distribute weather charts and similar graphic material to ships at sea"—*Buffalo Courier-Express* (such as the Pentagon's Bay of Pigs invasion fleet) fleet)

"The mainstream of pornography has to do with power—quite literally naked power"—*Small Press Review* #22 (as in Bayley/Ballard, the violent deaths of the Kennedys and Martin Luther King, as in the Pentagon's plan to invade Cuba.)

Euridice likes to bug me. "I cut the story on you out of the Courier, and threw it in the garbage."

"Hell, I'm really going to beat your ass."

Proposition. An African Bay of Pigs was planned in September, 1974. White insurgents seized R. Clube de Mozambique and broadcast appeals for help from neighboring countries. According to the *Johannesburg Star* "White mercenaries from South Africa were considering a drive into Mozambique to aid the rebels". About that time details of the Chile coup had surfaced, things were heating up much more than expected and the Mozambique plan was shelved.

(Nixon is murdering his universe—is that what the dates mean?)

According to E. Howard Hunt, then vice-president Nixon was the Bay of Pigs "action officer" within the White House (before losing the election to Kennedy). This is revealed in Hunt's book "Give Us This Day" which we reviewed earlier. ("Medical experts suggest that the vascular shock Mr. Nixon suffered on Tuesday could be induced not only by infection or a serious accident but by intense psychological stress"—Reuters)

"In those times a virgin might dine at the calf and drink at the eyes and sleep where she would and none would harm her...when those springs died and the New Mountains waned, the Belly, which had, scarcely noticed, waxed above the Loins, withered in one dark."—Gene Wolfe, "Peritonitis", *Frontiers* #1 (never mind the syntax—I'm sure everyone gets the point: Nixon is dying)

The ultimate product of these combined genres, i.e. science fiction and the private eye, is the super international agent as typified by the James Bond novels, the later works of Mickey Spillane and E. Howard Hunt's "The Venus Probe". About this species of literary mutant, M. John Harrison notes in *NWQ#3* "It lacks the craftsmanship and the vitality that runs through even the most mediocre science fiction, and simultaneously exhibits the coarse, simplified approached that has dogged the genre since its Popular Mechanics days".

("Girl, get your ass over here". Thrush and Nixon both inhabit the same universe)

About The Torch in *Marvel Mystery Comics*—"Carl Burgos dreamed up a character who was supposed to have been produced by the ever-present, well-intentioned scientist. In this case the scientist invented an android who burst into flame and concidentally came to life when exposed to oxygen"—Les Daniels in *Comix* (Like The Torch, Nixon has already become a myth so I really don't know how this will end.)

(He prays to Reverend Kludd
The high priest of anti-matter.)

"By sub-culture we mean one which is separated from the mainstream of the arts, philosophy, religion, or generally accepted rules of social behavior. The schism can occur in all four areas, or in only one."—Thrush, *December*, Vol. 10

Thrush "realizes something that perhaps fellow Northamerican DXers do not. We cannot expect the world's governments to be free and open with information about their respective broadcasting configuration, as the CRTC and FCC are...Sometimes one must aggresively monitor and seek sources of information when official information is not forthcoming, or is at a variance with the facts. One wades through haystacks to find the needle of truth. Often the conclusions are erroneous."—*DX Monitor*

The private eyes are the real gurus (magicians) of this fucking universe. And it hasn't got anything to do with mystic highs or that kind of shit. You dig it up one piece at a time and eventually the puzzle begins to fit together. And you keep putting the damn thing together even when nobody really wants to look at it—even when there's no longer a buck in it.

A vision. Stars, planets, galaxies, the Universe expands to its outer limits, then the whole system begin to collapse upon itself like the black holes of anti-matter. Each billion years (each night?) the sky becomes a little brighter until the end when it explodes and everything is fire—an ash of anti-matter from which the conquest begins again. The Torch, Nixon, Thrush are reborn.

Euridice stands
Naked black
Woman myth
Become flesh

> *Working Hard*
> *Older*
> *Screw me, girl*
> *While you can]*

[*Somewhere in the bible*]
Fuck me, woman, I'm your man. God damn it, I'm a man.
> *[END]*

A New Macedonian Empire

(The power people will wait no longer. The Joint Chiefs of Staff, the CIA, Pope Ironside all want answers and I don't have any. I will have to shoot my own script and pass it off as the real thing)

Alexander the Great, circa 350 BC, established the first Macedonian empire. In 1975 AD two clandestine transmitter sites, one in Canada and another in the U.S. (not too far from Robert Houston's WKDN), were about to establish a second—anti-matter variety. At the very least, it all adds up to some pretty exotic DX. NEW MYTH: Alexander the Great was the son of a Macedonian king and the beautiful enchantress from outer space, Titania. Orpheus was one of Alexander's generals and accompanied him on his expeditions to Africa (where he layed Euridice) and India where Alexander was fatally bitten by the primordial spider, Purusha. By the 20th century their descendents all found themselves in Canada (shortly after the fall of Richard Nixon there were 55,000 Macedonians living in southern Ontario).

Additional Macedonian shortwave transmissions were aired from a site in Portugal shared with Radio Canada International, secretly owned by the Voice of Germany, and ultimately linked to the Pentagon through the North Atlantic Treaty Organization. Nixon is a direct descendent of Alexander the Great (as were Adolph Hitler and Count Dracula). Further, according to an as yet unverified report, Robert Houston was one of Nixon's illegitimate sons (again by Titania). This based on an unpublished *Candid Press* account (however the documentation here may have been forged by the White House plumbers as part of their attempt to insure clemency). In any event, Robert Houston (or whatever his real name) was determined to regain control of America's space program. The Macedonian network served as a front for his activities.

Houston/Hunt/Heath brood(s) in Canada
Dream(s) of another Radio Americas
A Radio Americas LIBRE

99

Another missile crisis

Another invasion.

(The poor bastards who actually operated the Canadian station probably didn't have the foggiest notion what they were into.)

"A clandestine international broadcast station has been operating secretly from the Niagara Peninsula. These radio transmissions consisting of Greek and Middle Eastern music have been heard throughout the North American continent on the 90 metre shortwave band, while a Hamilton monitor has reported 'local reception' near the top of the standard AM radio dial."—*Niagara Falls Review*

("AM"—layman's term for Medium Frequency although in a strict technical sense it refers only to a type of modulation)

"The desire for political rehabilitation and acceptance, his acquaintances say, appears to be the subject most constantly on Mr. Nixon's mind. His moods shift suddenly, and sometimes puzzlingly, from buoyant confidence to spells of withdrawn, almost sullen reflection interspersed with bursts of angry impatience over the rate of his physical recovery and the state of his finances.'"— *New York Times*

(Kill the mother fucker)

The real purpose of Bahia Cochinas was to prevent Communist radio reception of rocket firings from Cape Canaveral. Until the election of John F. Kennedy, Richard Nixon was the Bay of Pigs action officer within the White House. Except for a few patriots such as Hunt and Houston (who were actually on the Pentagon's payroll anyway), most of the CIA were Kennedy men. Kennedy further endangered the space program by not invading Cuba during the missile crisis.

(Orpheus Thrush, a renegade CIA agent, was the secret source of that *Niagara Falls Review* story)

"The DXing hobby is so much of a diversion away from politics, national and otherwise, and the associated problems of a somewhat hectic atmosphere. Those so inclined should pursue it more at leisure. I'm engaged in a bit of research into various aspects of MF phenomenon—there are so many mechanisms little understood, or envisioned by the average DXer concerning propagation, aurora, horizon blockage, fortuitous reception, noise absorption, or the physical parameters of loop antenna, all of which demand attention."

—Houston Roberts

"Whether or not the sunspot count has any practical effect on the weather, it definitely affects the ionosphere. Once every 11 years solar activity and sunspots drop to an absolute minimum. Although the next low is not expected until 1976, the ionosphere is already doing strange things to international radio reception"—

—*Popular Electronics*, Dec. 1973

By 1975 DXing had become a form of UFOlogy. "Mr. Roberts received his S.B. from Titan Institute of Technology in 1964. He enrolled as a graduate student in Electrical Engineering from 1964 to June 1968 but received *no* graduate degree. I have checked with physics and they have informed me that he did not receive any graduate degree from them. There are no records anywhere indicating that he was employed as a research or teaching assistant on faculty".

CANADA GOES CLANDESTINE   Up until last fall few DXers would have considered either Canada itself or any individual Canadian station as "exotic". Then a bizarre pair of duplicate transmissions appeared on the scene. First a station appeared on the 90 meter band and was heard at times over two thirds of the continent with "Greek & Near East" music. This one has now developed into a miniature Radio Americas/Swan affair. To refresh memories (if that really is necessary) DXers went around in the 1960s batting each other's brains out over whether or not RA was on Swan Island. The answer turned out to be both: its primary site was Swan but alternate sites were planned and the Radio Americas identity did emanate from other locations during the Cuban missile crisis (more complete details are in the Oct. 74 PE). With our current mystery, the question is—does it or does it not come from Canada? Again the answer is both.

The 90 meter signal is the harmonic of a station presently varying between 1583 and 1586 kHz. Anytime of the day it is on (currently weekends only) the variable 1586 signal can be detected at Monitoring Station November and an Arctic Shortwave Club member has reported local reception in Hamilton. Meanwhile a second transmitter, with exactly the same format, has been heard a number of evenings on a frequency varying between 1614 and 1620 kHz. This apparently does emanate from the NE U.S. site recently referred to by Glotz in *DX News*; however, so far as we can determine it has no 90M harmonic.

One of the various chains of events set in motion by the people at Radio Swan/Americas culminated in Watergate. Let's hope its contemporary Canadian counterpart turns out to be what Prime Minister Trudeau would call a "fun day".

(Richard Nixon was fatally bitten by the primordial spider)

[*"Don't fuck with me. I can hardly pay my bills. You live in a dream world over there. I've got to pay $49.50 just to keep them from hauling away my furniture. I can't even buy myself a pair of stockings or a drink when I want it. If you could get yourself a white bitch you wouldn't want me anyway. I'm not in the mood for playing games"*]

"The secret ambition of a great many shortwave listeners is to singlehandedly uncover a piece of international intrigue. The radio waves themselves offer tremendous opportunities to do just that. For example, beginning with a single piece of unusual transmission during the Cuban missile crisis, when Radio Americas switched IDs with VOA sites (including the historic one at Brentwood, now of ITT SW facsimile fame) we determined that it was primarily a military, rather than a CIA, operation. We further learned that it was capable of transmitting from secret locations other than its publicized Swan Island site. Now these conclusions have been confirmed by none other than E. Howard Hunt of Watergate fame."   —Orpheus in *Popular Electronics*

[*It's too late. I'm too far into it to quit. I have fixed the relationship between anti-matter and reality. I am the world's first shortwave guru. Either I make it big now, all the money Euridice can spend, or I'm not going to make it at all.*]

22nd day of the 11th month—President John F. Kennedy died
from an assassin's bullet
4th day of the 4th month—Martin Luther King Jr. assassinated
6th day of the 6th month—Robert F. Kennedy died from an
assassin's bullet
8th day of the 8th month—Richard M. Nixon announced his resignation as President of the United States

By 1975 Nixon was on his way to martyrdom as planned but the CIA had regained control of the space program (I could work Vice President Rockefeller's name in here). According to the Larousse *World Mythology*, without myth Alexander would never have undertaken the conquest of the East. Better a dead martyr than a live crook. Once the man is dead you can build on his myth.

(Conceive at 12
The man is drunk
Black history)

Pope Ironside will have to abandon his celibacy cover. Dispatch a cable from Titan to Heaven. Give him time to get the suckers used to the idea. Meanwhile back on 20th century Earth the Commies were about to use the CIA to infiltrate America's space program. Before Watergate it had been planned that the joint U.S./Soviet mission would end in disaster and Moscow would be blamed for it. But McCord rewrote the script.

The Pentagon's Portuguese site peddled salvation in Macedonian. "The Universe and everything in it, even you, repeats every 82 billion years".

(Just keep fucking)

"Join Titania's army and escape Purusha's pupposeless cycle of creation. March with the virgin mother of a new Universe. Kill a commie for Christ."

("To invoke a super counter-myth, is Purusha himself a sadistic maniac"—SPR#22. For the purposes of this fiction, Purusha's web is the Gutenberg galaxy, a print universe)

Orpheus, for reasons of his onw, rejected the Macedonian cult of Titania (he hoped to sell an expose which would pay off some of Euridice's bills) and thereby accidentally founded the Church of the True America ("The United States of America was the beginning of the restoration of the Kingdom of God in the Universe and was therefore cleansed of all things that offend and of them which is iniquity....America fill the Universe with fruit!"), now headed by Ironside.

(Gutenberg began with the bible didn't he?)

(This should get me off the hook with the crippled bastard at least.)

(Ironside envisions himself as myth—a legendary high priest of Inner Earth City saving it from space hoaxes.)

All hail Purusha

The only true creator

of Anti-matter

"Orpheus was the original private eye. He went into the underworld in search of Euridice. But he didn't know when to quit digging." —*SPR#22*. Titania's new universe was anti-matter emanating from the *Radio-TV Experimenter* mixed with additional print radiation from *Popular Electronics* at the Gutenberg/broadcast interface. As the date of the joint U.S./Soviet space mission approached, Orpheus and Houston found themselves locked in a struggle for control of Titania's universe.

(Orpheus found Titania, a beautiful but almost transparent (in this respect not unlike Howard Hunt's mistresses) humanoid Wonder Woman planning to conquer Earth by infiltrating its power structures with radio broadcast controlled androids)

"A bill to make it illegal to degrade, mutilate, desecrate or insult the Canadian flag moved one step closer to parliamentary approval yesterday"—*Toronto Globe & Mail*, Feb. 19, 1975. At 0440 UT that date the Macedonian station supposedly operating from a site in the northeastern U.S. signed off with "U.S.". signed off with "Oh Canada". THE ELECTRONICS BUFF—IN SPACE   Beginning with the joint U.S./Soviet mission, however it turns out, and culminating with the first American inner-planetray landing, international interest in space exploration is on the rebound. Which means that while almost everything else about hobby electronics has changed, shortwave listening continues as a basic. What is the world hearing and saying about our space program??? Fortunately, those stations with the answers to that question—Voice of America, Radio Moscow, Armed Forces Radio & Television Service, Radio Habana Cuba, Radio Canada International, Radio Americas Libre, are easily tuned on the simplest of shortwave receivers.

[*When Orpheus met Euridice she was hustling at the Thessaloniki Bar on Pine Street. The old Greek bastard who owned it was fucking a black woman but didn't want his kid to marry a nigger*]

The basics of the Houston plan were known to both the CIA and Orpheus. One of the Macedonian transmitters would send an especially coded telemetery signal on a secret Pentagon control channel which would kill the docking astro/cosmonauts with poison gas. But only Houston knew which site would be used for that purpose, as well as the frequency (6000 kHz) and the hiding place of the deadly pellets aboard the U.S. spacecraft,

(For this scenario I have spliced together several sequences from TV series of the 1960s. "Jean Luc Goddard began with Sam Spade and Philip Marlow, painter Mel Ramos turned *Cat Woman* (from the Batman comic strip) into a masterpiece while another comic-book character, Green Lantern, became the lead poem in LeRoy Jones' *Dead Lecturer* collection. And you too might become rich and famous within the next few years as one of this nation's leading pop art gurus—if you keep a close watch on local TV schedules and don't mind putting down that grand you'll need for a video tape recorder (VTR."—*December,* vol. 12)

INTERVIEWER: As so much of your writing involves international detective work, isn't there a danger of being carried away by the game?

ORPHEUS: Yes, there is. Every so often I find myself identifying with James Bond, or Ironside. But then I remind myself that most of the clandestine broadcast activities I've researched are pretty minor league stuff. LIke this pair of Macedonian stations I've been hearing for the past few months—one of them is in or near Hamilton—they'r probably just on the air for the fun of it.

(Euridice's losers. LeRoy with his voodoo, in the house on Pine Street. Thessaloniki's young greek, the white mother fucker (everything except fuck), in a flat on Illinois Avenue. Lying Willie, the pimp, a room in the Little Harlem Hotel. I'm the one who's going to make it.)

(I am a character in a piece of 20th century science fiction. Through the miracle of print I have been transported into the year 6000 and it is from this vantage point that I am able to re-examine my roots.)

Washington and Moscow, in order to save face, would blame each other for the space disaster and this would bring them to at least the brink of nuclear war. In the ensuing confusion, Houston's Macedonians planned to seize power in Canada while he would declare himself as the son of the martyred president, Nixon the peacemaker. In the event that the Macedonian network could not be destroyed by covert means before it interfered with CIA's space program (they were relying heavily on the Orpheus expose) the Central Intelligence Agency had made plans for an invasion of both Canada and Portugal.

(I have now arranged things so that both sides can claim legitimate motives. Liberals can support the CIA on humanitarian grounds while conservatives will continue to rally around the Joint Chiefs of Staff and General Houston. "Mass media utilizes the myths of the current pop culture, amplifies those myths and therefore modifies the pop (mass) culture itself."—*December*, vol. 12)

The CIA planned to use Soviet troops in Portugal, and Cuban-trained Quebec separatists in Canada. ("I wonder who you would've married if you weren't the way you are?") "In one version of the Hindu creation myth the deity Purusha, like a giant spider, secretes an interminable thread, weaves a web within it and then lives in this web."—*December*, vol. 15. For the purposes of this production, Purusha is himself a print creature.

In reality, the Portuguese civil war which broke out during the Apollo-Soyuz mission accomplished the same objective as the plånned space disaster. As Soyuz touched down safely on Earth—

"The Portuguese Socialist Party yesterday threw its full weight behind efforts to oust left-wing President Vasco Goncalves, as the country's military rulers set to tackle a deepening political crisis.... Anti-Communists continued to vent their feelings in the conservative north, destroying two of the Communist Party's headquarters and attacking two others. Gen. Otelo Saralva de Carvalho, head of the Capcon internal security forces, underlined the prevailing tension by saying his men were set to thwart any coup attempts."—

—*Toronto Globe* — *Mail*, July 15, 1975

As millions watched the Apollo landing on television, a warship sailed for a secessionist Portuguese island province. Unknown to the TV audience, poison gas was seeping into the spacecraft.

(There is just enough historical documentation to assure that the above cannot be refuted.)

In order to attract attention to his expose, and thus prevent an invasion of Canada, Orpheus deployed his concept of shortwave facsimile broadcasting as a new international mass media. "In the Australian magazine 'Electronics Today International'...(Orpheus) detailed the first practical system for reception of such broadcasts by the general public."—*Buffalo Courier Express*

(Pierre Eliot Trudeau is unmasked as one of Howard Hunt's androids)

(Black women seized by Titania's border guards)

(Nixonian rocket ships invade Inner Earth)

(Alexander rapes the lost continent)

(Titania strips off the Canadian flag, spreads her legs, and screws america.)   ("Seig Heil"

SPACE AGE EXPOSE INTENDED FOR FUTURE PRINT DISTRI-BUTION VIA SHORTWAVE FACSIMILE BROADCAST (from *December*, Vol. 13, 1973)

It was no accident that man first circled the Moon on Christmas eve. A statement from the Voice of America dated Feb. 24, 1969, concerning all-night operations commencing at Midnight GMT Dec. 24, 1968, reads as follows; "Because of the tremendous world interest in this first manned flight to the Moon, it was decided in early December that the VOA would cover the flight at various stages throughout the entire night".

In an inter-office memo dated Dec. 23, 1968, after the Apollo 8 blastoff on Dec. 21 to supervisory personnel in charge of a VOA relay, reference is made to "minro" changes in the relay's schedule to cover "important aspects of the Apollo flight mission" but a later memo acknowledges that "numerous" alterations were in fact made in the station's schedule to cover "all phases of the Apollo 8 moon shot". It's possible of course that the staff here was not told in advance of Washington's plans because of this particular station's "sensitive" location. But if the decision for all-out coverage, and therefore an all-out propaganda effort, had already been firmly made way back in December, it is hard to understand why any sort of secrecy was necessary at any relay site. Certainly advance notice on the resulting schedule alterations and transmitter site interchanges would have made everyone's job a little easier.

On the other hand, had Apollo 8 met with disaster before going into lunar orbit (as subsequently happened with Apollo 13) all-out coverage could—with only a few senior officials knowing it had been planned—have been quietly scrubbed or at least, again as in the Apollo 13 crisis, postponed until the outcome of the mission had been determined with reasonable certainty.

(One of the transmitter sites involved in these Apollo 8 interchanges is also used by Radio Canada International.) (Is that the Portuguese transmitter site which later became part of Houston's Macedonian empire? I don't know.)

Does it matter? The tape is finished.

I am on my way back to Heaven.

I have promised Euridice that I will return to Titan in a month and I call her every night. "Are you having your supper?"

"Yes". She doesn't really expect to see me again.

"Maybe tomorrow night I'll call you a little later". There should be a pretty good payoff from both sides. [She takes off her dress

    (I'd sell my soul   to turn him on
    for the truth)   for 100 dollars) On the flight
I spend my nights DXing broadcasts from Earth.
    (Down country roads   Radio Canada International
    Where white girls   Voice of America
    Screwed   Radio Free Macedonia
    and were no wiser   anti-matter
    Canada—the last white bastion) According to the Hamilton
station it has begun to snow.   *Roll, mama*
    One last spring?   *You've got the Cadilac*
    (Nixon is coming again)   *But we'll survive*
                             Promises of what

Houston/Hunt/Heath brood[s] in Canada   could be
Dream[s] of another Radio Americas
A Radio Americas LIBRE
Another missile crisis
Another invasion.

                            (Fade)

ANTI-MATTER   A Glossary of Abbreviations, Names, and
Historical Figures

Alexander the great	King of Macedonia
Allende, Salvador	President of Chile
AM	Layman's term for Medium Frequency, although in a strict, technical sense it refers only to a type of modulation.
ASC	American Security Council
Ballard, J.G.	British SF writer
Bayley, William	British SF writer
BBC	British Broadcasting Corp.
BCB	A range of electromatic frequencies normally used only for local and regional sound broadcasting, a portion of the Medium Frequency spectrum.
Bennett, Hank	Former shortwave editor of Popular Electronics.
Bradbury, Ray	U.S. SF writer
Burroughs, William	U.S. writer
Butterfield, Alexander	revealed the existence of Nixon tapes
Castro, Fidel	Premier of Cuba
CFC	Committee for a Free Cuba, right-wing anti-Castro organization tied to Radio Americas and Radio Caribe.
CFAP	Council for Fascism and Astrological Progress
CIA	Central Intelligence Agency, major power center in U.S. hierarchy.

CP	Candid Press, a pornographic newspaper
Cp's	Cerebral palsey victims
Christ, Jesus	Founder of the Christian church, later fictionalized by a variety of political factions.
CRC	Cuban Revolutionary Council (organized by E. Howard Hunt)
December	Chicago based literary press and magazine.
DX	A form of escapism popular in the mid 20th century involving the reception of distant or rare electromagnetic radiation.
EI	Electronics Illustrated, a magazine
Elwood, Roger	U.S. SF editor
ETI	Electronics Today International, a magazine.
FAX	(SW FAX) facsimilie broadcasting, i.e. transmission of still pictures, charts, graphics etc. via (shortwave radio
FBI	Federal Bureau of Investigation
FEBC	Far East Broadcasting Company, a missionary organization which once carried the Radio Americas Libre program.
G-2	U.S. Army intelligence
Gates	Manufacturer of radio transmitters
Gilbert, Dan	Radio evangelist
Giordano, Walter	Robert Houston contact
Glotz, Capt.	(aka Capt. Guts) DX sub-culture-comic book character.
GMT	Greenwich Mean Time
Graham, Billy	Radio evangelist
HCJB	A missionary shortwave radio station at Quito, Ecuador
Heath, Horton H.	"Commercial Manager" of Radio Swan
Herbert, Frank	U.S. SF writer
Higgins, Dick	Literary theorist
Hitler, Adolph	Chief of State, Nazi Germany

Holmes, Sherlock	British detective
Houston, Robert	Employee of Radio Americas
Hunt, E. Howard	Prolific writer of spy novels, right wing CIA agent on Pentagon payroll, key figure in Bay of Pigs and Watergate.
IDs	Identities of radio stations
Interchangeable IDs	Of both radio stations and characters.
IGB	Intergalactic Bat
Ironside, Robert	TV paraplegic detective played by actor who simultaneously played Pope on special Easter program
ITT	International Telephone & Telegraph
ITU	Illusionary Television Universe, a future plan for world control by a secret government on the Moon
Jack the ripper	Victorian psychopath
Johnson, Curt	Editor and publisher of December, former RTVE editor
Kennedy, John F.	President of the United States
Kennedy, Robert F.	JFK's brother, 1968 presidential candidate
King, Martin Luther, Jr.	U.S. religious and civil rights leader
kHz	kiloHertz, measurement of electromagnetic frequency
KIA	Kalahari Intelligence Agency
Kirkbride, K.C.	Author of article on anti-matter in RTVE
Kludd, Reverend	Evangelist created by William Bayley
Knight, Gladys	(and the Pips) Soul music group
Kostelanetz, Richard	Literary theorist
KW	Kilowatt, measurement of transmitter power
Leminitzer, Gen. Lyman	High ranking member ASC, also on Rockefeller Commission
LF	Low Frequency (30-300 kHz)
LRSP	League for Racial and Spiritual Purity

Malzberg, Barry	U.S. SF writer
McCord, James	Former CIA agent, member Committee to Investigate Assassinations, destroyed original Watergate coverup.
McLuhan, Marshall	Canadian communications prophet
MF	Medium Frequency (300-3000 kHz)
MHz	MegaHertz (1000 kHz)
MI	Mechanix Illustrated, a magazine
Moorcock, Michael	British SF editor and writer, founder of New Worlds (Quarterly)
Moriarty, Professor	Arch enemy of Sherlock Holmes
NATO	North Atlantic Treaty Organization
Nixon, Richard	President of the United States
NNRC	Newark News Radio Club
NPACT	Liberal Washington-based public TV organization
NSS	Key U.S. Navy shortwave communications Station in Maryland
NWQ	New Worlds Quarterly
NYRB	New York Review of Books
Oswald, Lee Harvey	Probable assassin of John F. Kennedy, circumstantially linked to the Committee for a Free Cuba, Cuban Revolutionary Council, Radio Americas, Radio Caribe, Radio Free Russia and Radio Libertad
OTH	Over-the-horizon (shortwave) radar
PE	Popular Electronics, a magazine
Pentagon	Conquerers of space, key agency in military-industrial economy, tendency toward right wing religion, rival of CIA
Poirier, Richard	Literary critic
Pournelle, Jerry	U.S. SF writer
Prouty, L. Fletcher	Former military intelligence man, public relations expert, and writer
Pynchon, Thomas	U.S. writer, prophet
QSL	A card, letter or other form of printed matter confirming DX reception
RA	Radio Americas

RAL	Radio Americas Libre, a right wing political broadcast organization operated by the ASC.
RCI	Radio Canada International
Radio Caribe	Station in the Dominican Republic with clandestine links, founded by Rafael Trujillo
Radio Free Russia	Linked with Radio Caribe and Radio Libertad
Radio Libertad	Clandestine shortwave station, linked with Radio Swan and Radio Caribe, probably first operated as Radio Escambre Libre at conclusion of Bay of Pigs fiasco, eventually taken over by Radio Free Russia
RS	Radio Swan, radio station with main transmitter site on Swan Island, part of the Bay of Pigs operation, later became Radio Americas
Rockefeller Commission	Panel appointed by President to investigate CIA.
RTVD	Radio-TV Dominicana, a station with historical links to Radio Caribe
RTVE	Radio-TV Experimenter, a magazine
shortwave	3-30 MHz
Silverberg, Robert	U.S. SF writer
Spillane, Mickey	U.S. writer
SPR	Small Press Review, a magazine
SR	The Saturday Review, a New York based literary magazine
SWFB	Shortwave Facsimile Broadcasting
Szulc, Tad	U.S. writer
THRUSH	A subversive TV organization
TIA	Technological Intelligence Agency
TIT	Titan Institute of Technology
Trudeau, Pierre Elliot	Prime Minister of Canada
Trujillo, Rafael	Dictator of Dominican Rep., assassinated with cooperation of CIA
UFOlogy	Knowledge of, study of, lore about, unidentified flying objects

113

UHF	Ultra High Frequency (300-3000 MHz)
UNCLE	TV counter-intelligence organization
USAF	U.S. Air Force
Verwoerd, H.F.	Prime Minister of South Africa
VHF	Very High Frequency (30-300 MHz)
Vidal, Gore	U.S. writer
VOA	Voice of America
VOG	Voice of Germany
Vonnegut, Kurt, Jr.	U.S. SF writer
Wallek, Lee	Literary critic
WDSI	Call letters of Brentwood station when it operated as a VOA facility
WFIG	Radio station at Sumter, S.C., former employer of Horton H. Heath (Howard Hunt???)
WKDN	Station at Camden, N.J., former employer of Robert Houston, FM outlet later became part of a religious network which broadcast FEBC fund raising program
WMAL	The Evening Star Broadcasting Company, Washington, D.C.
Wonder Woman	Comic book character tied to Greek mythology